NEIL DIAMOND ANTHOLOGY

Contents

Edited by Will Schmid

HAL•LEONARD®
CORPORATION

7777 W. BLUEMOUND RD. P.O. BOX 13819 MILWAUKEE, WI 53213

PLAYING GUIDE

The songs in this Hal Leonard EASY GUITAR collection are presented with easy-to-read music and lyrics. Chord frames are given to aid the player with left-hand fingerings; however, intermediate and advanced players should feel free to use bar chords or other more advanced chord forms.

These arrangements reflect the style of the original recordings and are presented in easy-to-play keys. You may wish to sing some songs an octave lower than written and/or use a capo to adjust the level to your voice range.

Below the title you will find **strums** and **finger picks** which can be used with each song. See page 3 for an explanation of these symbols.

SAMPLE

SONG SUNG BLUE

Words and Music by
NEIL DIAMOND

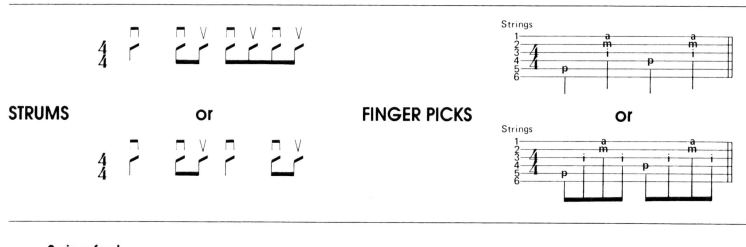

STRUMS   or   **FINGER PICKS**   or

Swing feel

Song   sung   blue,   ev - 'ry - bod - y knows   one.

STRUMS AND FINGER PICKS

Finger picks and strums are written out at the top of each arrangement. The system used throughout all **Hal Leonard Guitar** books is explained below

FINGER PICKING
The fingers are named p, i, m, a in the following manner:

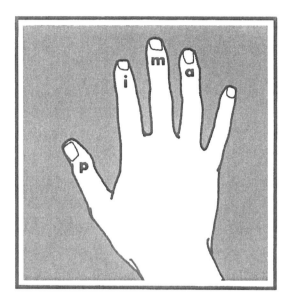

- The thumb (p) plucks strings 4, 5, or 6 depending upon which string is the root of the chord. This motion is a downward stroke. Use the left side of the thumb and thumbnail.
- The other fingers (i, m, a) pluck the string in an upward stroke with the fleshy tip of the finger and fingernail.
- The index finger (i) always plucks string 3.
- The middle finger (m) always plucks string 2.
- The ring finger (a) always plucks string 1.

The thumb and each finger must pluck only one string per stroke and not brush over several strings. (This would be a strum.) Let the strings ring throughout the duration of the chord.

Strums
The Strum symbols and their meanings are as follows:

⊓ — Down stroke

V — Up stroke

X — Dampening with the hand

FOREVER IN BLUE JEANS

Words and Music by
NEIL DIAMOND & RICHARD BENNETT

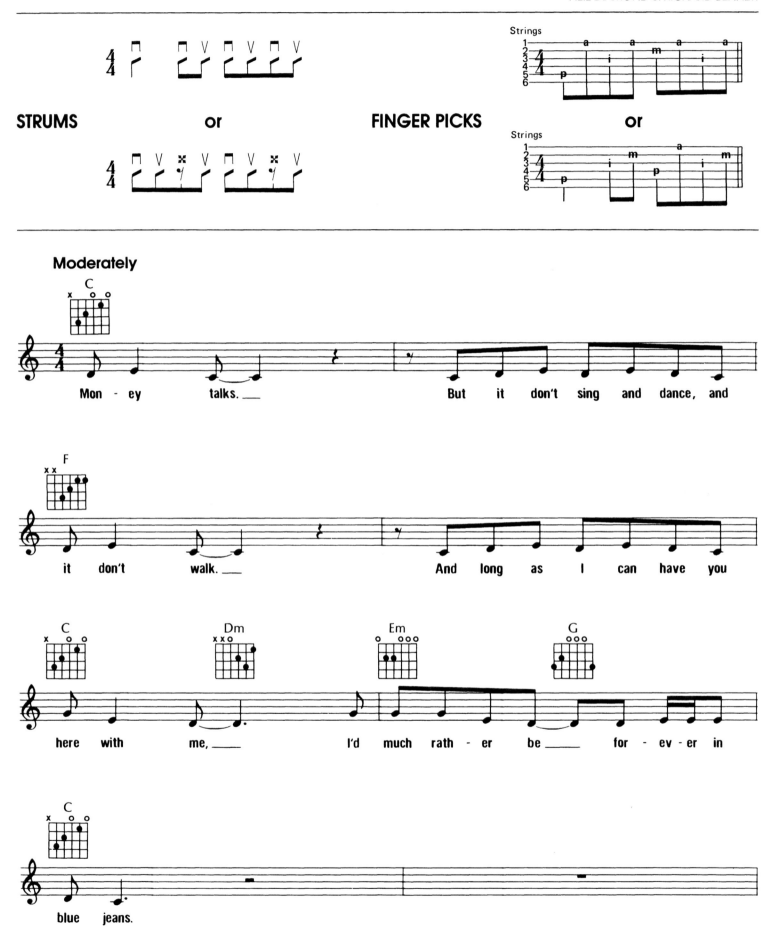

Hon - ey's sweet, __ but it ain't noth - ing next to

bab - by's treat. __ And if you par - don me, I'd

like to say __ we'll do o - kay, __ for - ev - er in

blue jeans.

May - be to - night. __ May - be to - night,

__ you and I __ all a - lone __ by the fire __

7

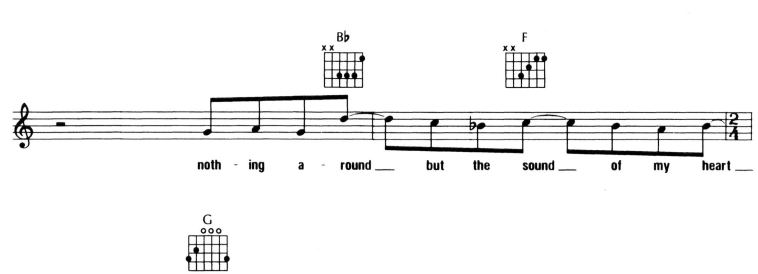

noth - ing a - round ___ but the sound ___ of my heart ___

___ and your sighs. ___

Mon - ey talks, ___ But it can't sing and dance and

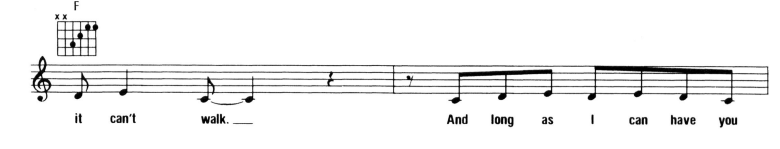

it can't walk. ___ And long as I can have you

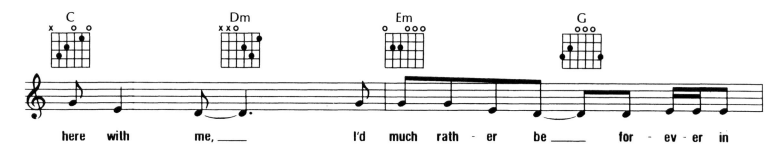

here with me, ___ I'd much rath - er be ___ for - ev - er in

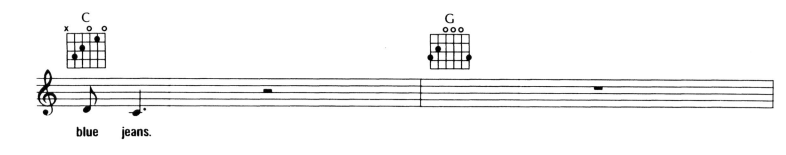

blue jeans.

C

Hon - ey's   sweet, ___   But   it   ain't   noth - in'   next   to

F

ba - by's   treat. ___   And   if   you   par - don   me,   I'd

C   Dm   Em   G

like   to   say ___   we'll   do   o - kay, ___   for - ev - er   in

C

blue   jeans,   babe. ___
blue   jeans,   babe. ___

F

And   if   you   par - don   me,   I'd
And   long   as   I   can   have   you

C   Dm   Em   G

                                                    Repeat and Fade

like   to   say ___   we'll   do   o - kay, ___   for - ev - er   in
here   with   me ___   I'd   much   rather   be ___   for - ev - er   in

9

YESTERDAY'S SONGS

Words and Music by
NEIL DIAMOND

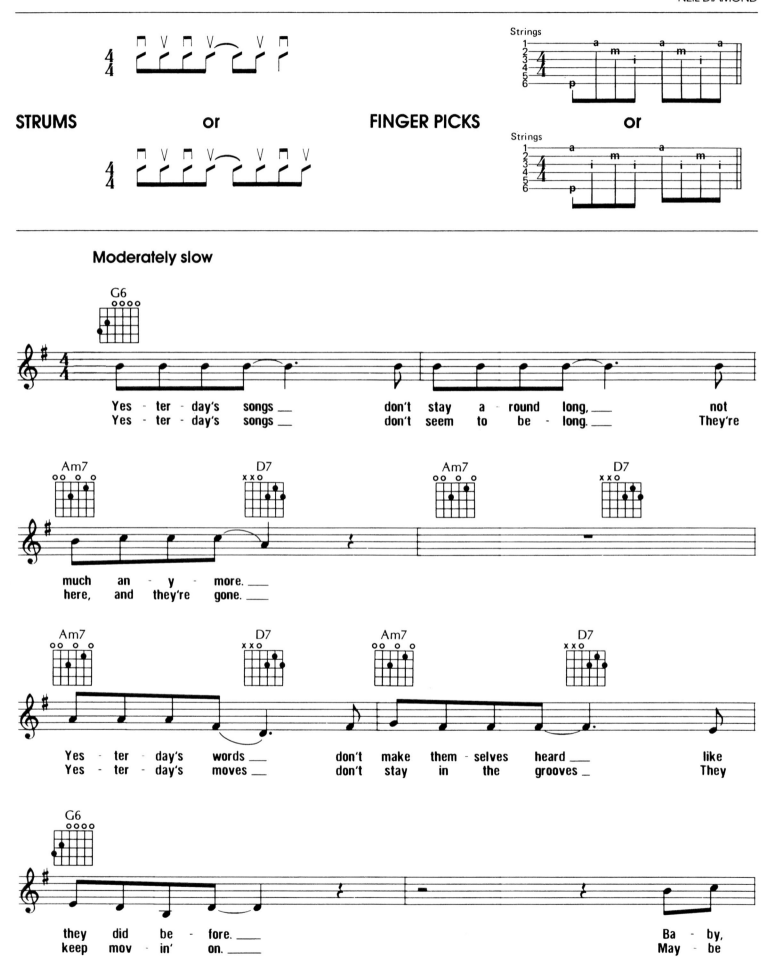

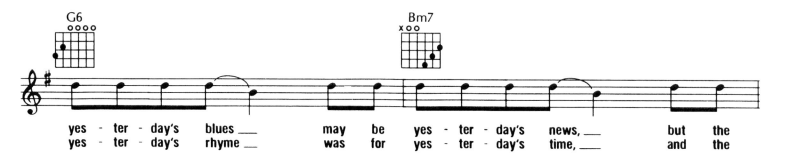

yes - ter - day's blues ___ may be yes - ter - day's news, ___ but the
yes - ter - day's rhyme ___ was for yes - ter - day's time, ___ and the

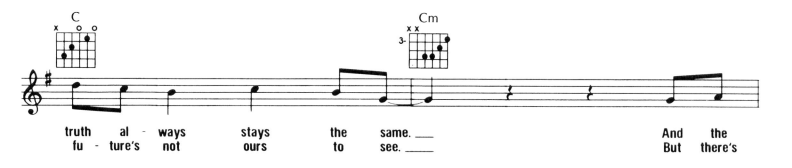

truth al - ways stays the same. ___ And the
fu - ture's not ours to see. ___ But there's

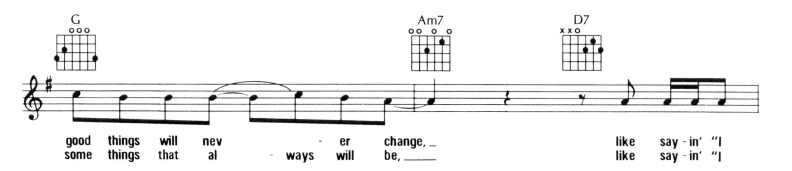

good things will nev - er change, _ like say - in' "I
some things that al - ways will be, ___ like say - in' "I

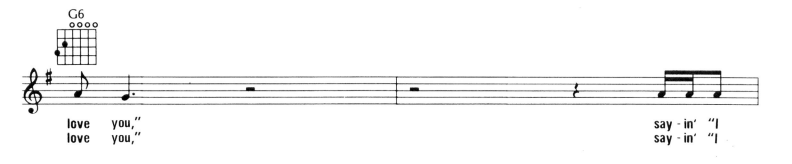

love you," say - in' "I
love you," say - in' "I

love you."
love you."

11

SWEET CAROLINE

Words and Music by
NEIL DIAMOND

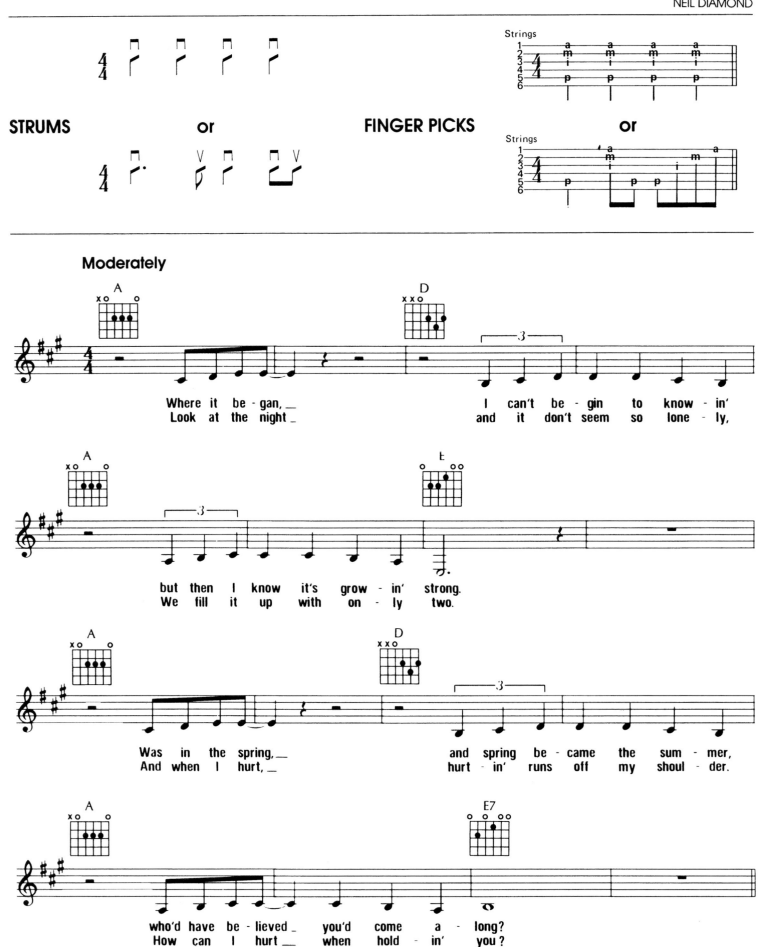

SEPTEMBER MORN

Words and Music by
NEIL DIAMOND & GILBERT BECAUD

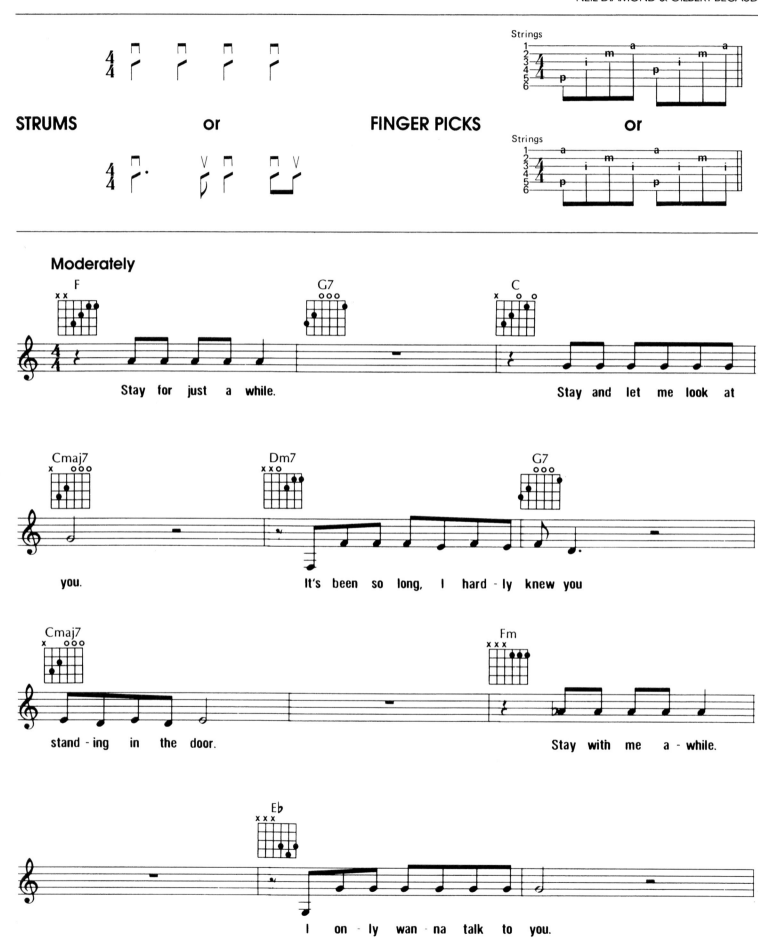

STRUMS   or   FINGER PICKS   or

Moderately

F   G7   C

Stay for just a while.   Stay and let me look at

Cmaj7   Dm7   G7

you.   It's been so long, I hard - ly knew you

Cmaj7   Fm

stand - ing in the door.   Stay with me a - while.

Eb

I on - ly wan - na talk to you.

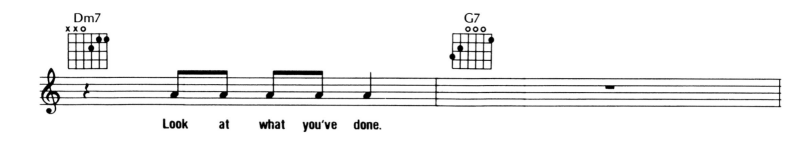

Look at what you've done.

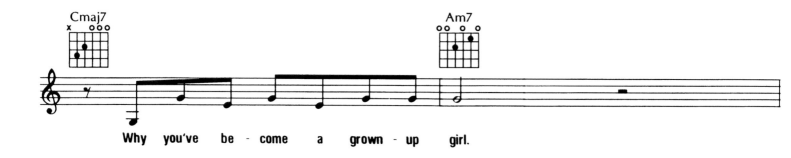

Why you've be - come a grown - up girl.

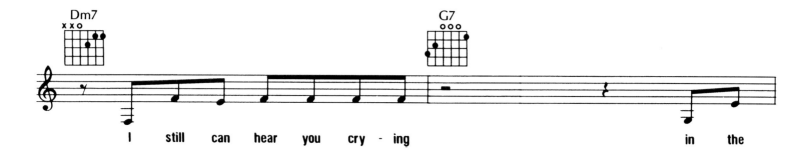

I still can hear you cry - ing in the

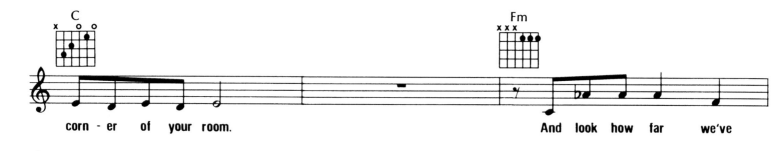

corn - er of your room. And look how far we've

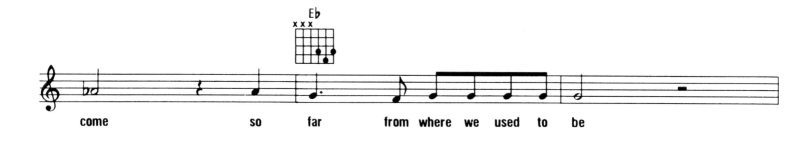

come so far from where we used to be

but not so far that we've for - got - ten

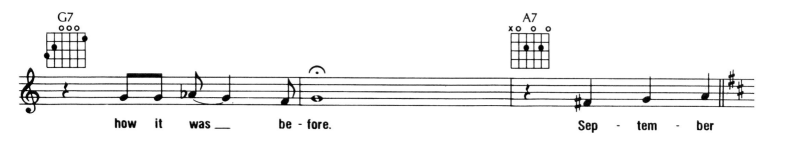
how it was ___ be - fore.   Sep - tem - ber

morn,   do you re - mem - ber   how   we

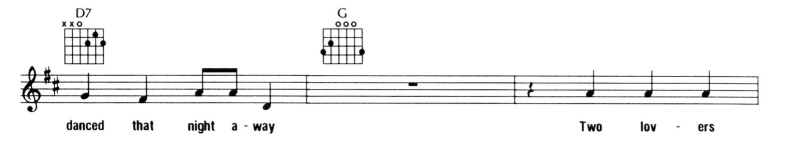
danced   that   night a - way   Two   lov - ers

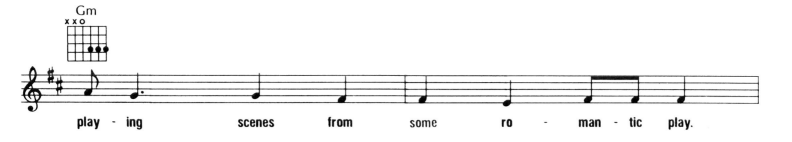
play - ing   scenes   from   some   ro - man - tic   play.

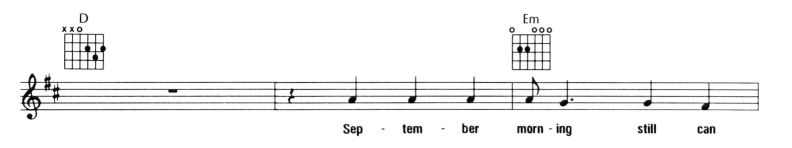
Sep - tem - ber   morn - ing   still   can

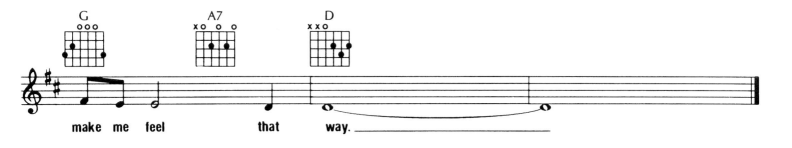
make me feel   that   way. ___

SONG SUNG BLUE

Words and Music by
NEIL DIAMOND

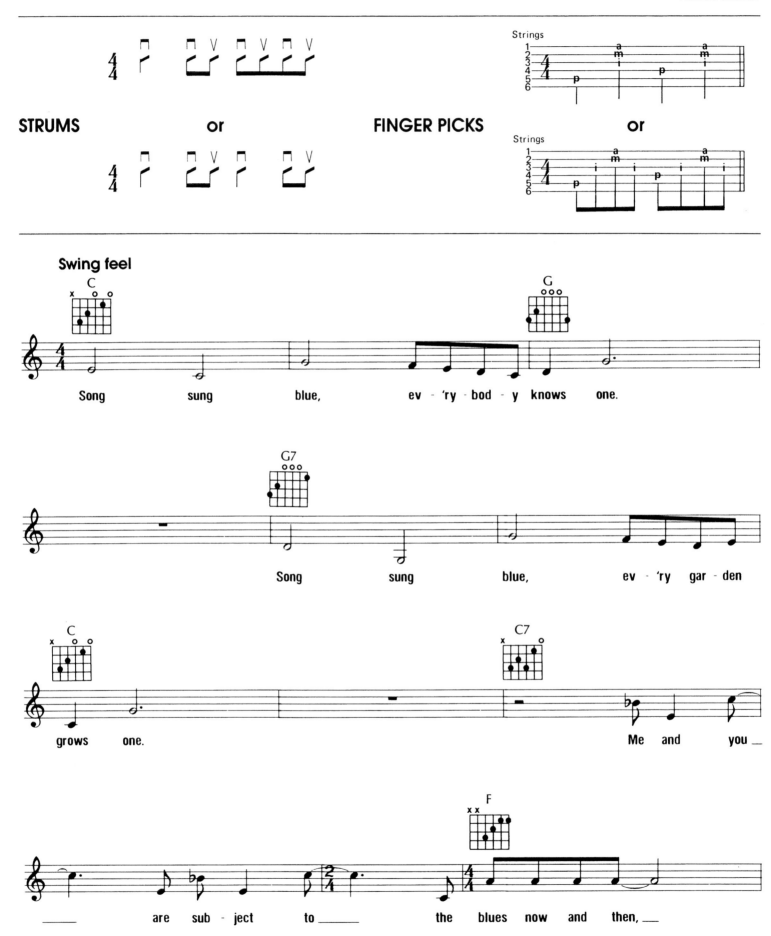

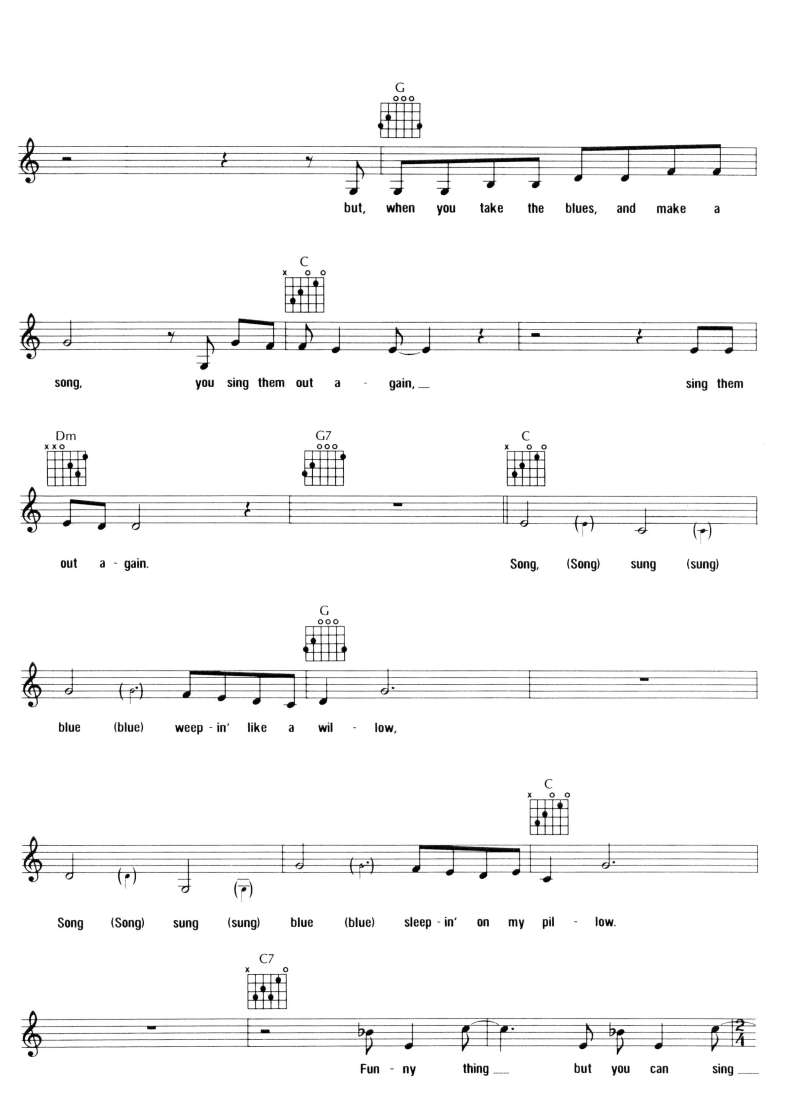

but, when you take the blues, and make a

song, you sing them out a - gain, ___ sing them

out a - gain. Song, (Song) sung (sung)

blue (blue) weep - in' like a wil - low,

Song (Song) sung (sung) blue (blue) sleep - in' on my pil - low.

Fun - ny thing ___ but you can sing ___

_____ it with a cry in your voice, ___

And be - fore you know you're feel - in' good,   you sim - ply got no choice

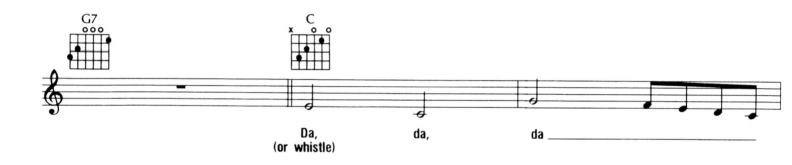

Da,   da,   da _____
(or whistle)

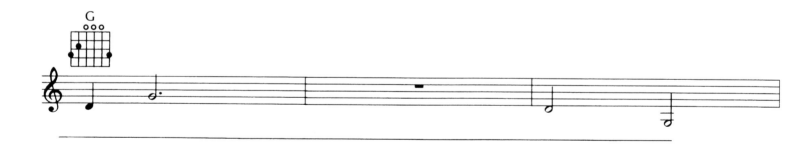

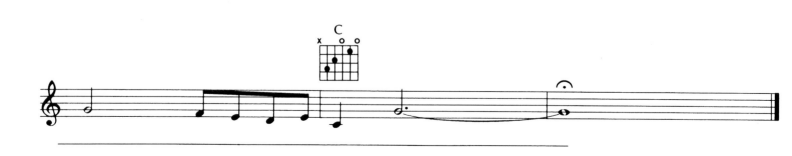

YOU DON'T BRING ME FLOWERS

Words by NEIL DIAMOND,
MARILYN BERGMAN & ALAN BERGMAN
Music by NEIL DIAMOND

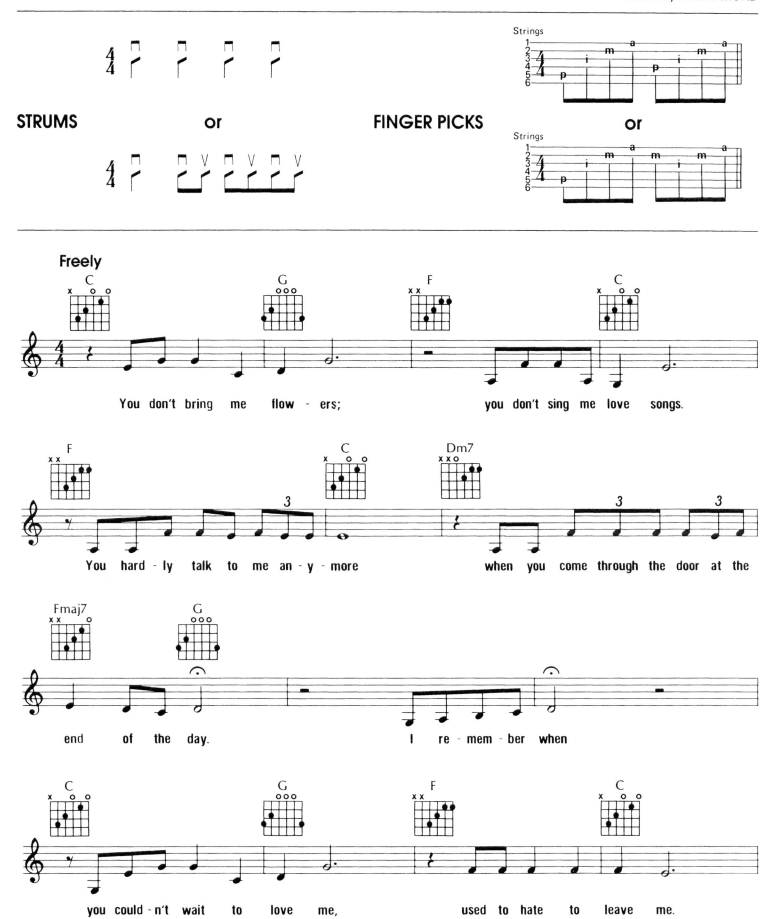

count an - y - more. _ They just lay on the floor till we sweep them a - way.

And ba - by I re - mem ber all the things you taught me:

I learned how to laugh and I learned how to cry. Well, I

learned how to love, e - ven learned how to lie. You'd

think I could learn how to tell you good - bye,

'cause you don't bring me flow - ers an - y - more. _____

SOOLAIMON

Words and Music by
NEIL DIAMOND

STRUMS   or   **FINGER PICKS**   or

Moderately

Come ____ she ____ come ____ say, ____
Bring ____ home _ my ____ name, ____

Ride ____ on the night.
on ____ the wings of a flea.

____ Sun ____ be - come
____ Wind ____ in the

day, ____ Day ____
plain, ____ Dance, ____

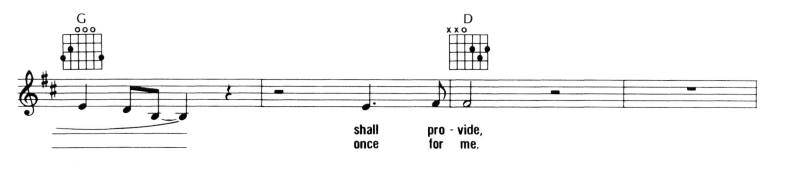

shall pro - vide,
once for me.

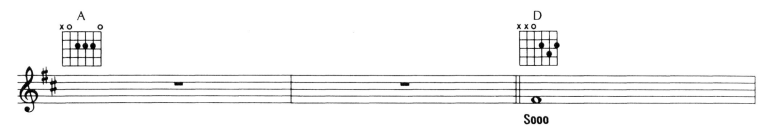

Sooo

Soo - lai - mon, ___ Soo - lai, Soo - lai Soo - lai - mon.

Soo Soo - lai - mon. ___ Soo - lai, Soo - lai, Soo -

- lai - mon. Sooo Soo - lai - mon. ___

Soo - lai, Soo - lai, Soo - lai - mon.

25

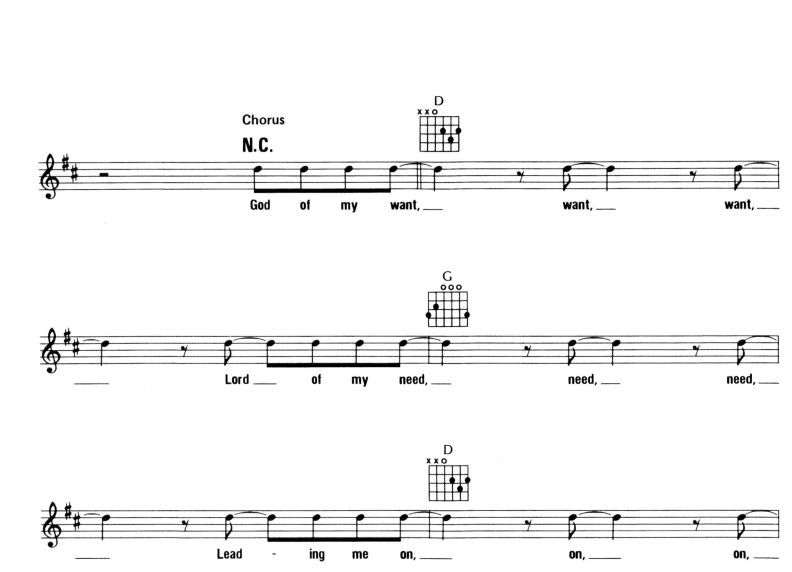

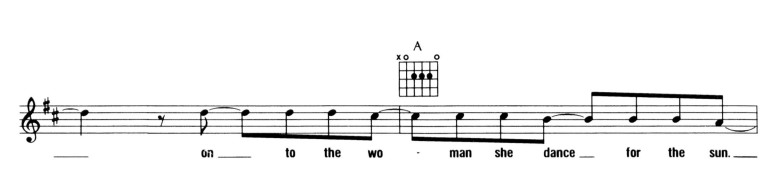

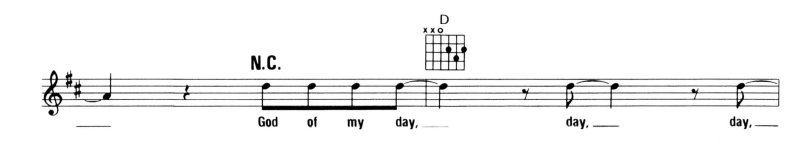

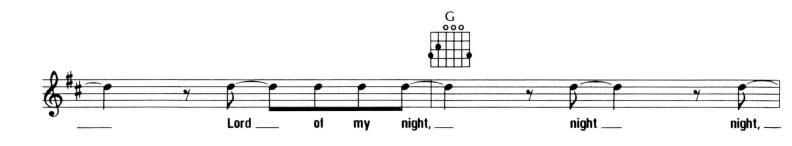

DESIRÉE

Words and Music by
NEIL DIAMOND

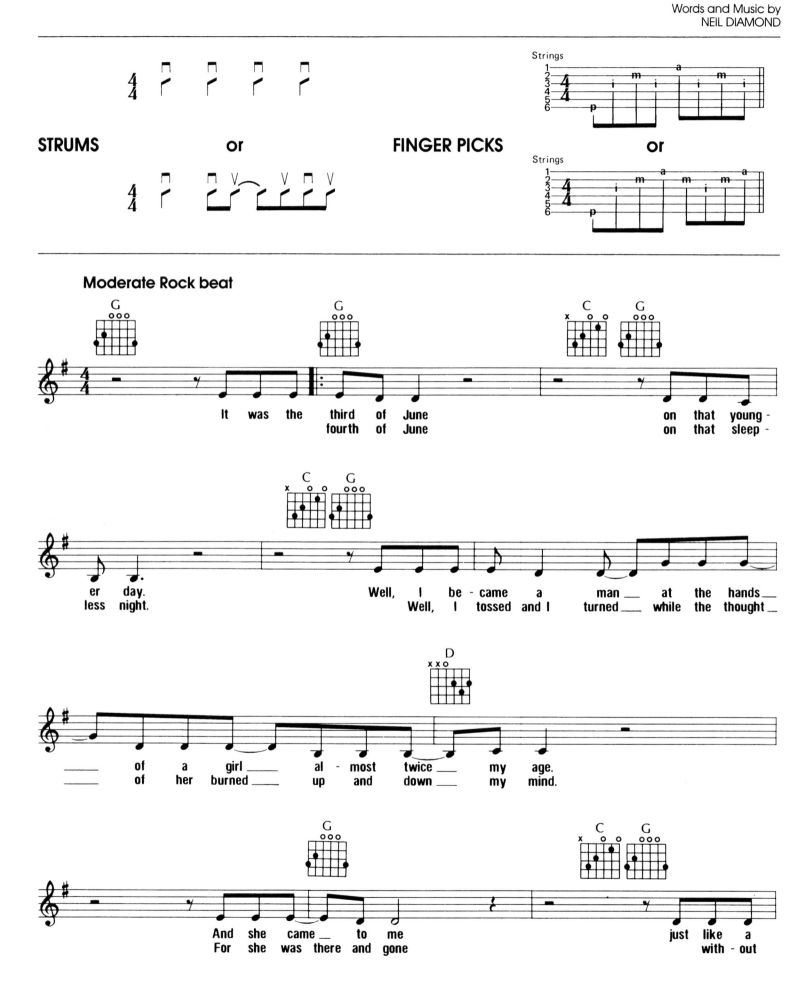

STRUMS   or   FINGER PICKS   or

Moderate Rock beat

It was the third of June
fourth of June
on that young-
on that sleep-

er day.
less night.
Well, I be - came a man __ at the hands __
Well, I tossed and I turned __ while the thought __

__ of a girl ____ al - most twice __ my age.
__ of her burned ____ up and down __ my mind.

And she came __ to me
For she was there and gone
just like a
with - out

morn - ing sun,
one re - gret,

and it was - n't so much _ her words _
but she con - tin - ues _ on _ like the

_____ as such _____ as the way they were sung. _____
words of a song I could not for - get. _____

It was the way they were sung. _
I could not for - get. _

De -

- si - ree, oh De - si - ree,

there I was found by the sweet pas - sion sound of your lov -

ing song. Time was right, the night was long.

Re - mem - ber De - si - ree, oh De - si - ree.

Some - how I knew I could on - ly have you till the

morn - ing light.

If on - ly for that sin - gle night,
The night was long, the time was right.

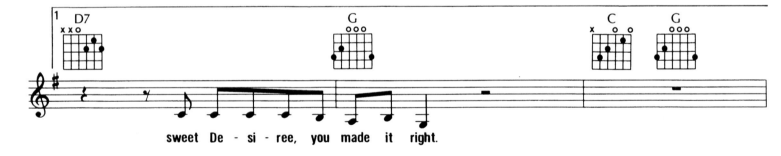

sweet De - si - ree, you made it right.

Then came the   Do you re - mem - ber,

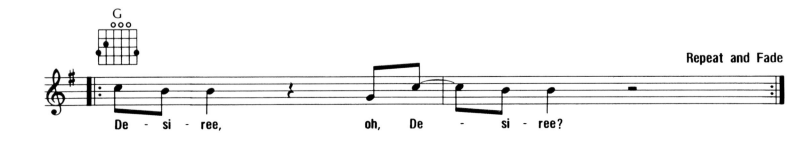

Repeat and Fade

De - si - ree,   oh, De - si - ree?

CRACKLIN' ROSIE

Words and Music by
NEIL DIAMOND

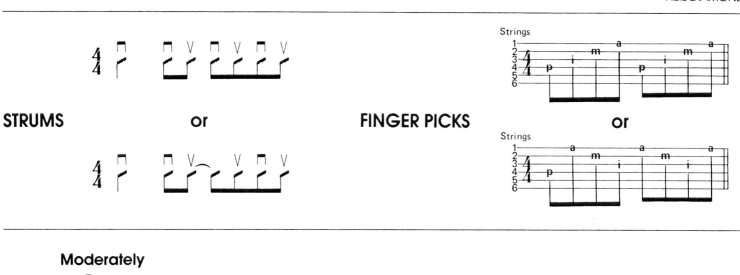

STRUMS   or   FINGER PICKS   or

Moderately

Crack - lin' Ros - ie get on board, ___

we're gon - na ride ___ 'til there ain't ___ no more to

go. Tak - in' it slow, ___ And Lord, don't you

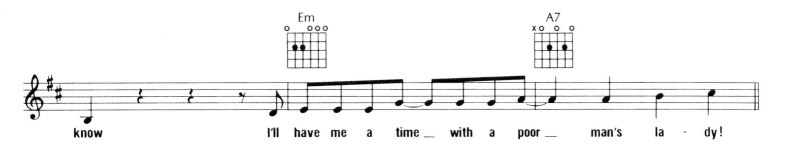

know I'll have me a time ___ with a poor ___ man's la - dy!

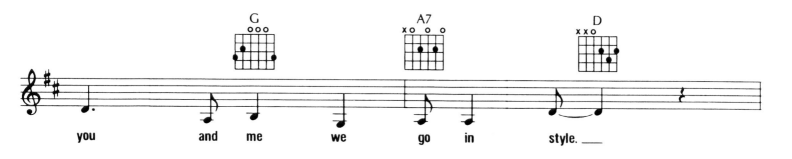

you and me we go in style.____

Crack - l - in' Rose,____ you're a store____ bought wom - an, but

you make me feel ____ like a gui - tar hum - min'. So

hang on to me,____ girl, our song ____ keeps run - nin' on. _____

_____ Play it now!____ Play it now!____

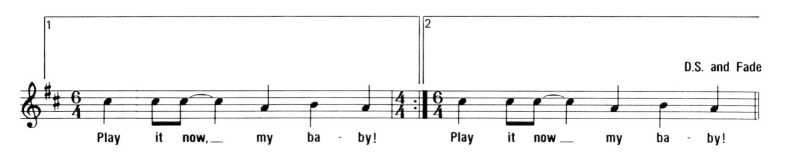

Play it now,____ my ba - by! Play it now ____ my ba - by!

33

I AM. . .I SAID

Words and Music by
NEIL DIAMOND

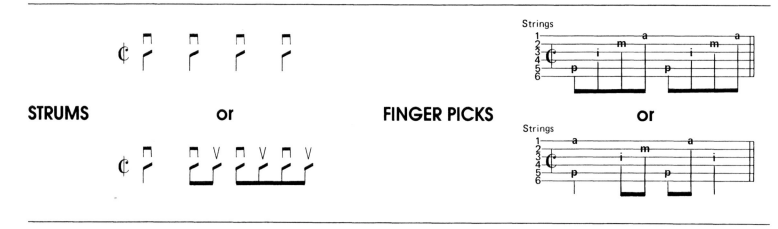

STRUMS   or   **FINGER PICKS**   or

In 2

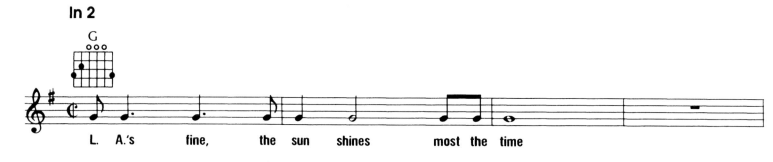

L. A.'s fine, the sun shines most the time

and the feel-in' is lay back,

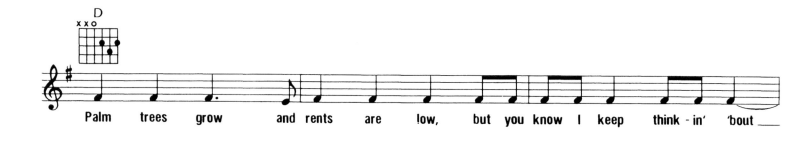

Palm trees grow and rents are low, but you know I keep think-in' 'bout ___

___ mak-in' my way back. ___

Well, I'm New York Cit - y born and raised, but

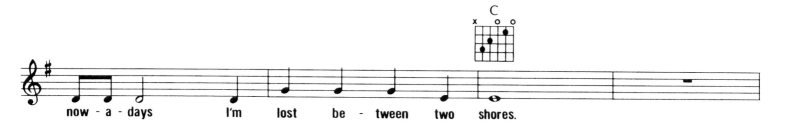

C

now - a - days I'm lost be - tween two shores.

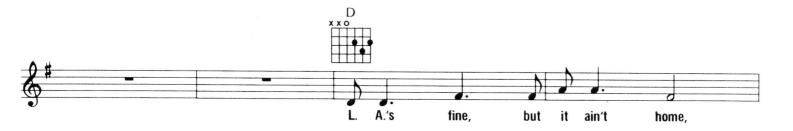

D

L. A.'s fine, but it ain't home,

D7   G

New York's home but it ain't mine, no ___ more. ___

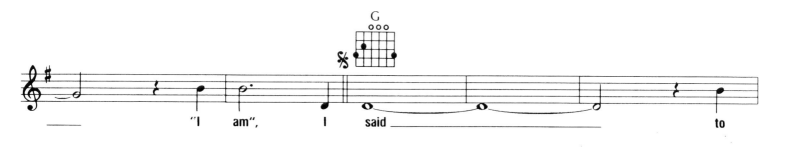

G

___ "I am", I said ___ to

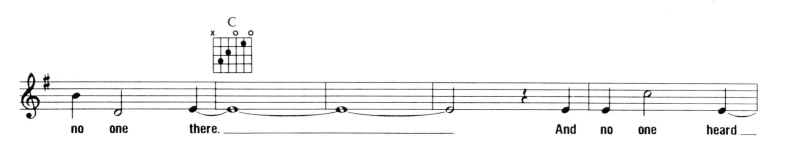

C

no one there. ___ And no one heard ___

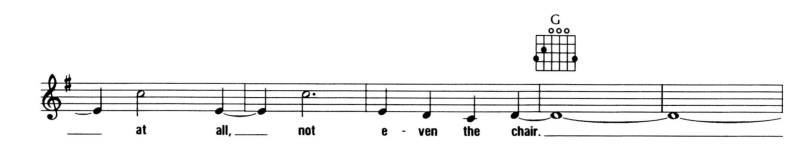

at all,_____ not e - ven the chair._____

_____ ."I am," I cried,_____ "I am," said I, __

_____ and I am lost ___ and I _____ can't

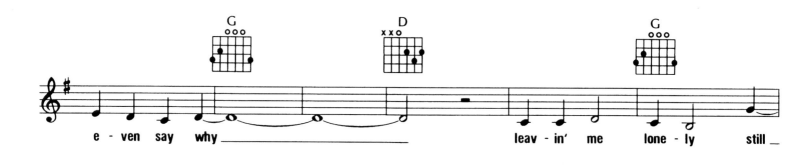

e - ven say why _____ leav - in' me lone - ly still __

FINE

_____ Did you ev - er read ___ a - bout a frog who dreamed___ of

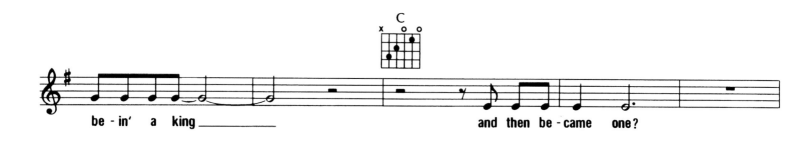

be - in' a king_____ and then be - came one?

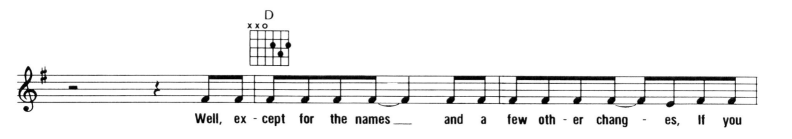

Well, ex - cept for the names ___ and a few oth - er chang - es, If you

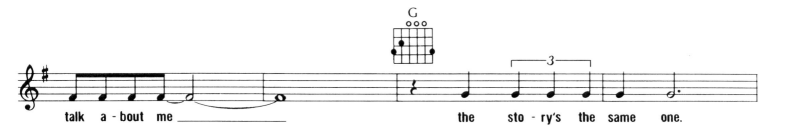

talk a - bout me _____ the sto - ry's the same one.

But I got an emp - ti - ness deep in - side,

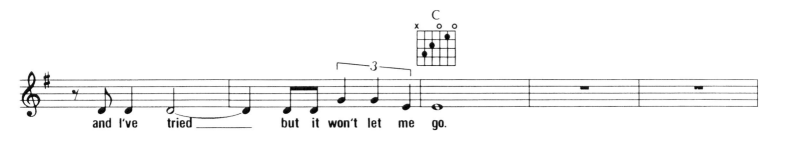

and I've tried _____ but it won't let me go.

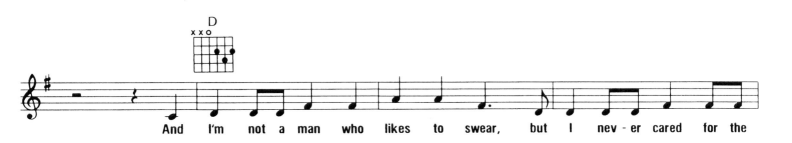

And I'm not a man who likes to swear, but I nev - er cared for the

D.S. al Fine

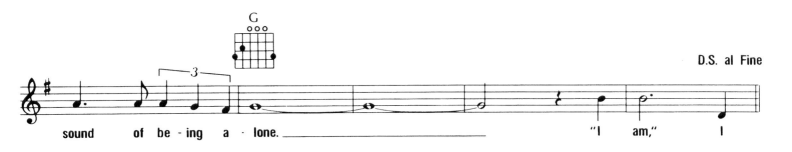

sound of be - ing a - lone. _____ "I am," I

37

BEAUTIFUL NOISE

Words and Music by
NEIL DIAMOND

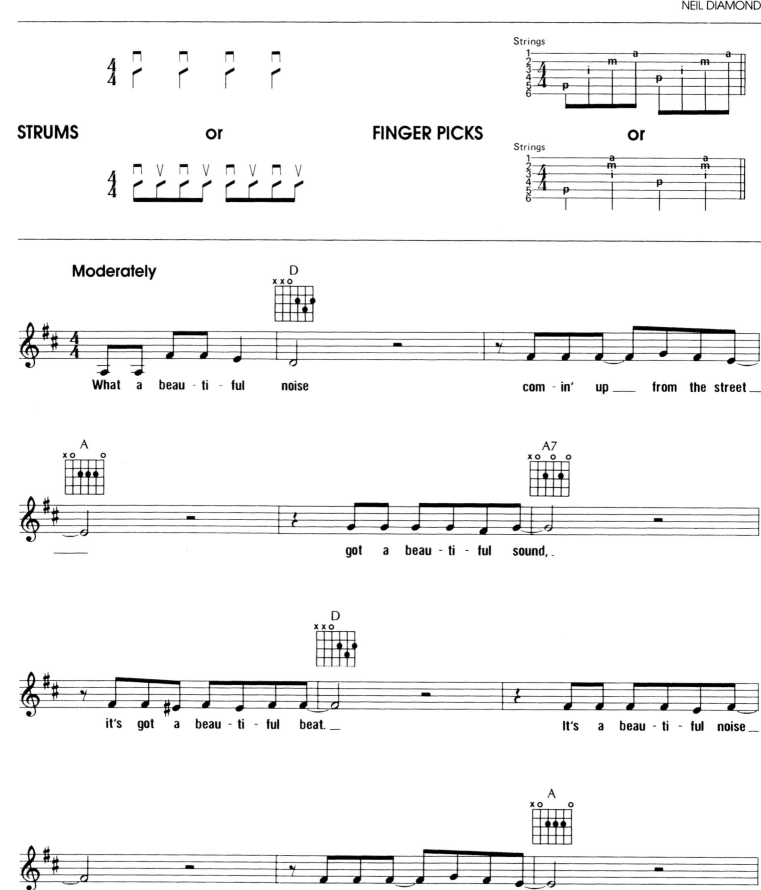

like the click - e - ty - clack ___ of a train ___ on a track ___

___ it's got rhy - thm to spare. ___ It's a beau - ti - ful noise ___

___ and it's a sound that I love,

and it fits me as well as a hand in a

glove, yes it does, ___ yes it does. ___

___ What a beau - ti - ful

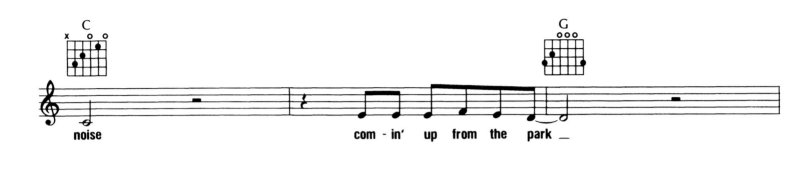

noise   com - in' up from the park __

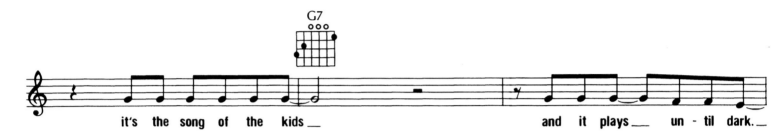

it's the song of the kids __   and it plays __ un - til dark. __

__   It's the song of the { cars / noise

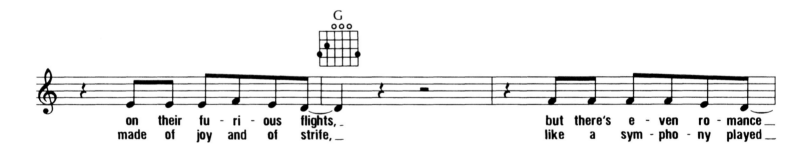

on their fu - ri - ous flights, __   but there's e - ven ro - mance __
made of joy and of strife, __   like a sym - pho - ny played __

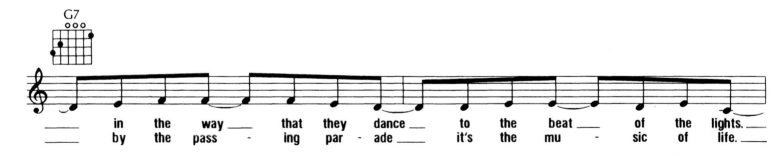

__ in the way __ that they dance __ to the beat __ of the lights. __
__ by the pass - ing par - ade __ it's the mu - sic of life.

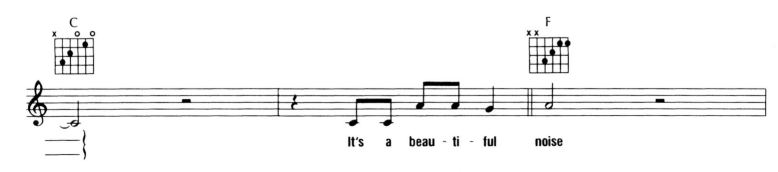

__ }   It's a beau - ti - ful noise

and it's a sound that I love

{ and it fits me as well__
{ and it makes me feel good__

{ as a hand in a glove,}
{ like a hand in a glove,}

yes, it does__

yes, it does. __

What a beau-ti-ful

noise

com - in' in - to my room__

and it's beg-gin' for me

just to give it a tune.

HE AIN'T HEAVY...HE'S MY BROTHER

Words and Music by
BOB RUSSELL & BOBBY SCOTT

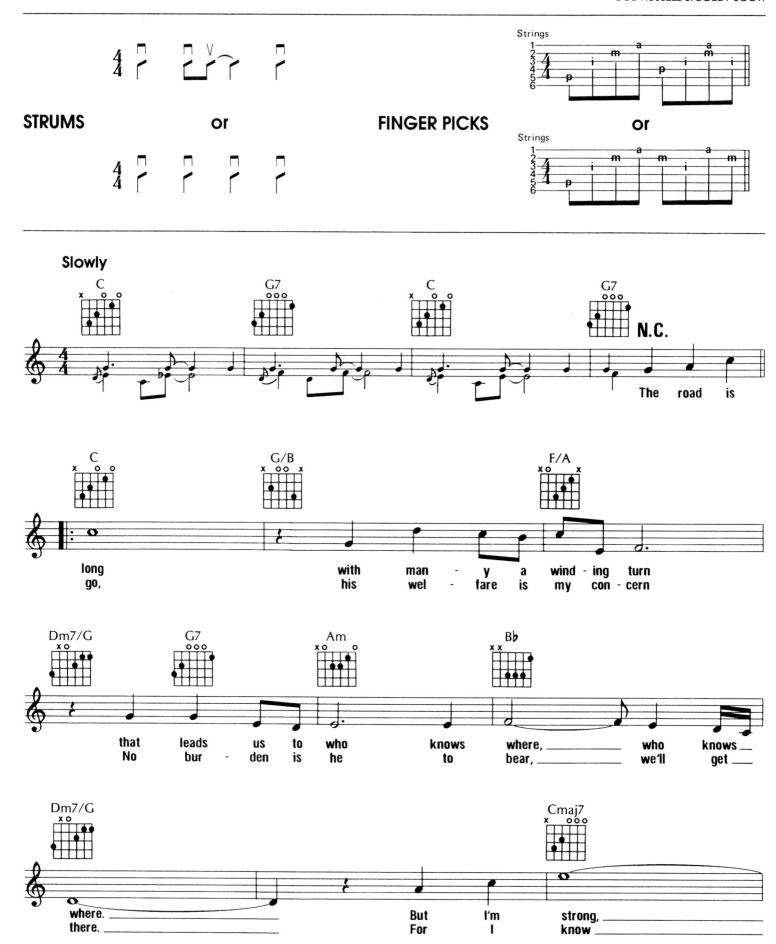

STRUMS   or   **FINGER PICKS**   or

Slowly

The road is long, with man-y a wind-ing turn

his wel-fare is my con-cern

that leads us to who knows where, who knows

No bur-den is he to bear, we'll get

where. there. But I'm strong, For I know

PLAY ME

Words and Music by
NEIL DIAMOND

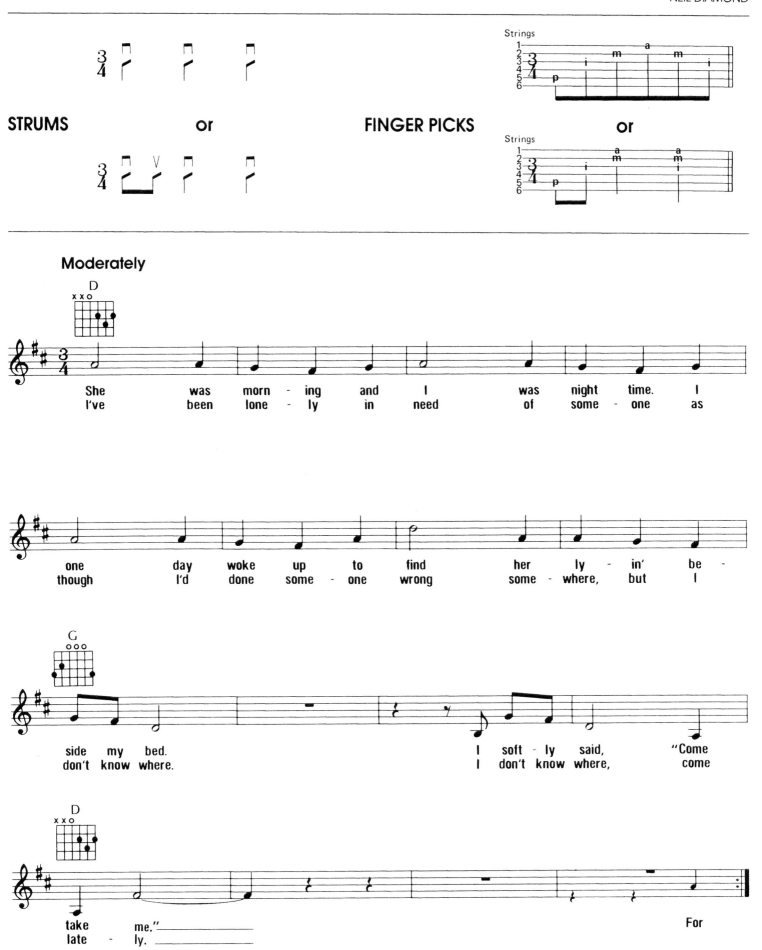

STRUMS   or   FINGER PICKS   or

Moderately

D

She   was   morn - ing   and   I   was   night   time.   I
I've   been   lone - ly   in   need   of   some - one   as

one   day   woke   up   to   find   her   ly - in'   be -
though   I'd   done   some - one   wrong   some - where,   but   I

G

side   my   bed.   I   soft - ly   said,   "Come
don't   know   where.   I   don't   know   where,   come

D

take   me."_____   For
late - ly._____

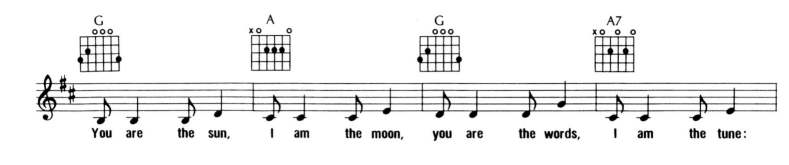

You are the sun, I am the moon, you are the words, I am the tune:

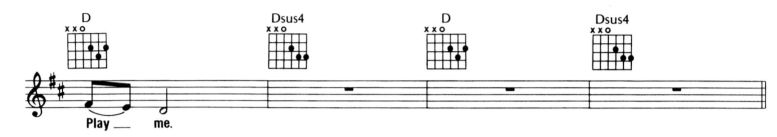

Play — me.

Song she sang to me, song she brang to me,

words that rang in me, rhyme that sprang from me

warmed the night. And what was right be —

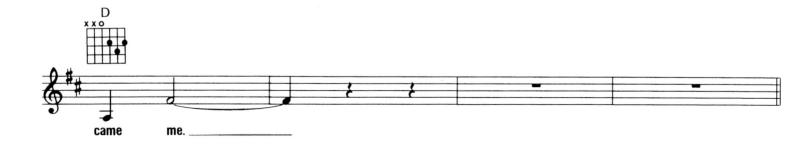

came me. _____

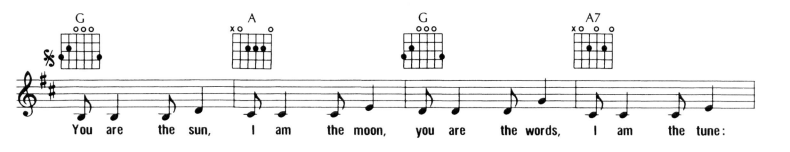

You are the sun, I am the moon, you are the words, I am the tune:

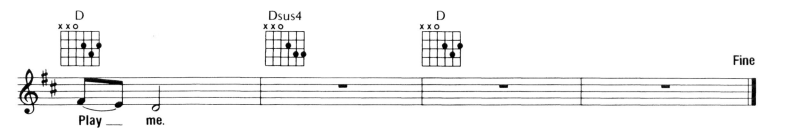

Fine

Play __ me.

So it was that I came to trav - el up -

on a road that was thorned and nar - row, an -

oth - er place, an - oth - er grace would

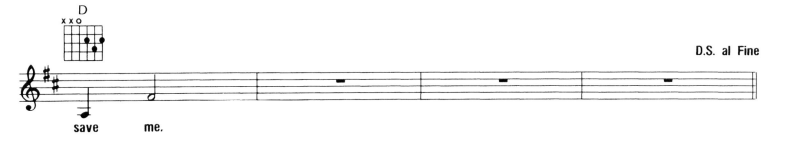

D.S. al Fine

save me.

IF YOU KNOW WHAT I MEAN

Words and Music by
NEIL DIAMOND

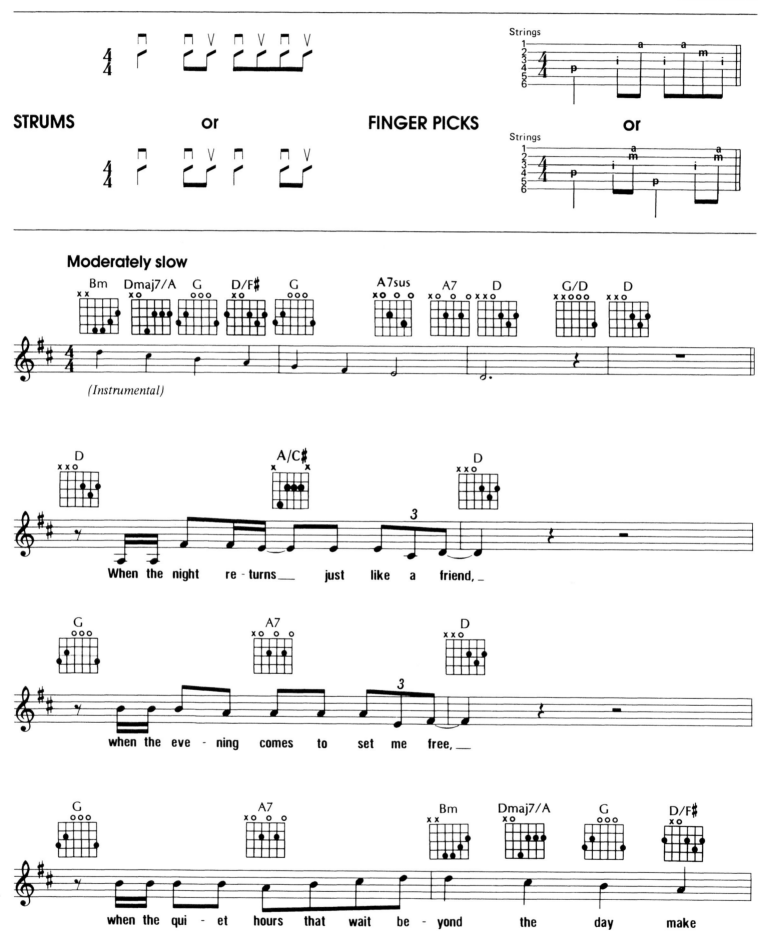

STRUMS   or   FINGER PICKS   or

Moderately slow

(Instrumental)

When the night re-turns___ just like a friend, _

when the eve - ning comes to set me free, ___

when the qui - et hours that wait be - yond the day make

Here's to the songs we used to sing, ___

and here's to the times we used ___ to know. ___

It's hard to hold them in our arms a - gain and hard to let them go. ___

D.S. al Coda

CODA

Do you   mean.

If you know what I mean.

BROTHER LOVE'S
TRAVELING SALVATION SHOW

Words and Music by
NEIL DIAMOND

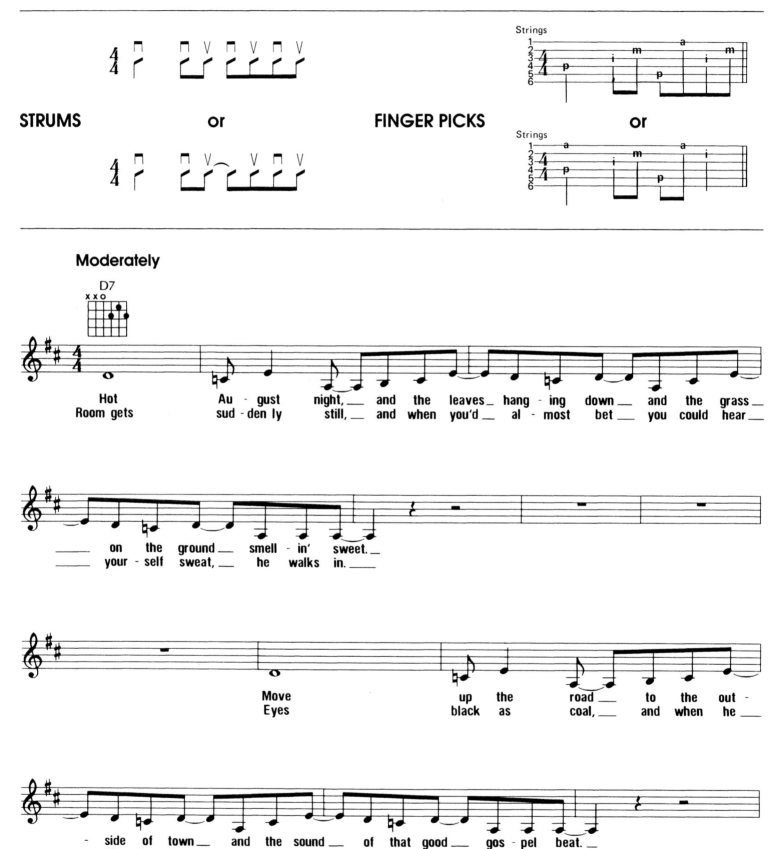

Bro - ther Love's Show.　　(Hal - le - lu - jah)

(Hal - le, Hal - le - lu - jah)　　(Hal - le - lu -

- jah)　　(Hal - le, Hal - le - lu - jah)

Take my hand __ in yours, __ 　　walk with me __

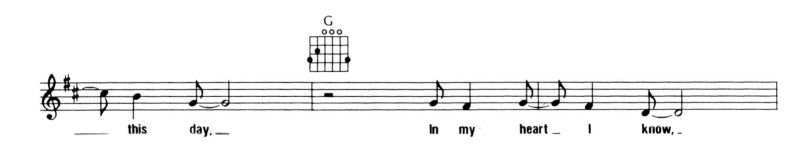

__ this day, __ 　　In my heart __ I know, __

I will nev - er stray. __ 　　Hal - le, hal - le, hal -

- le, hal - le, hal - le, hal - le, hal - le, hal - le,

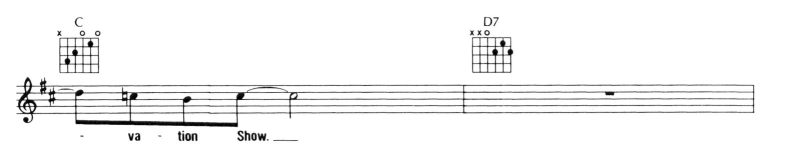

G

love, Broth - er Love, say, Broth - er Love's Tra - vel - ling Sal -

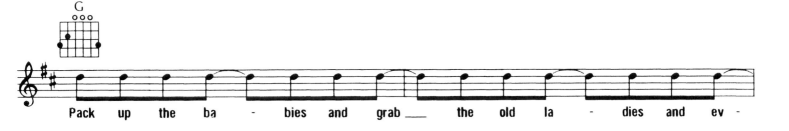

C   **D7**

- va - tion Show. ___

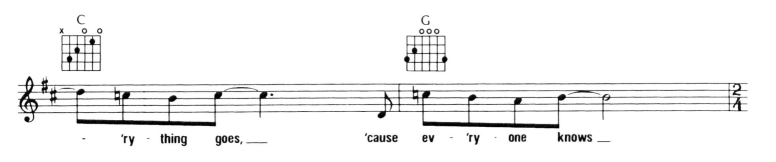

G

Pack up the ba - bies and grab ___ the old la - dies and ev -

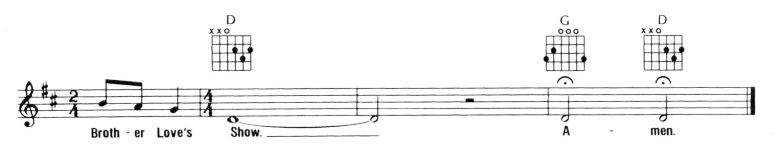

C   **G**

- 'ry - thing goes, ___   'cause ev - 'ry - one knows ___

D   **G**   **D**

Broth - er Love's Show. ___   A - men.

DEAR FATHER
(From JONATHAN LIVINGSTON SEAGULL, from the film by Hall Bartlett)

Words and Music by
NEIL DIAMOND

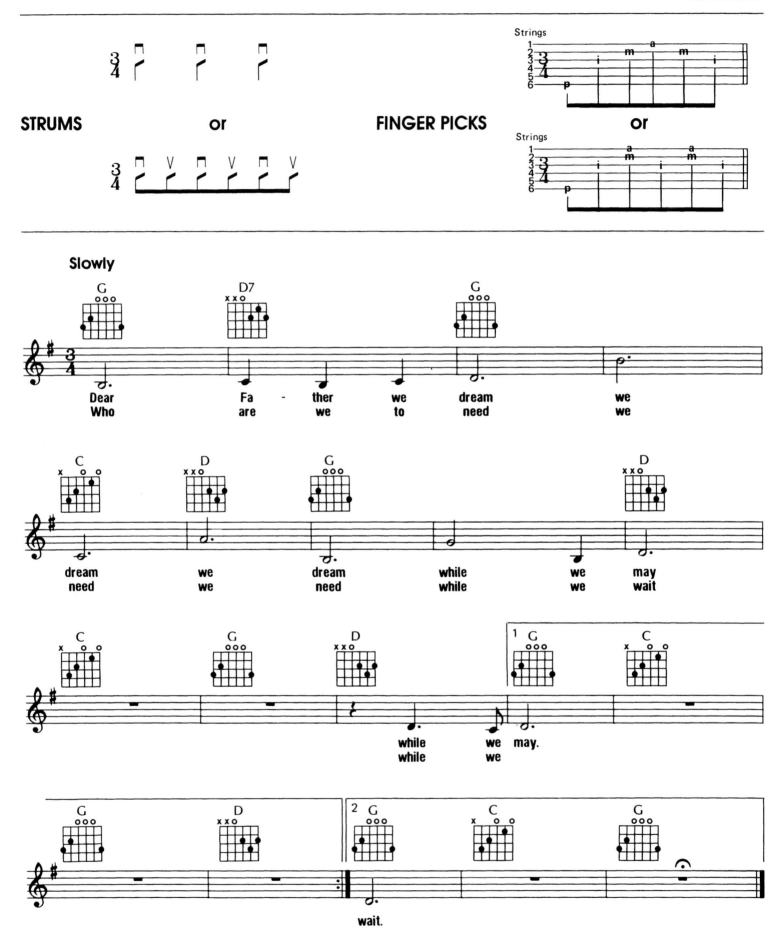

LONGFELLOW SERENADE

Words and Music by
NEIL DIAMOND

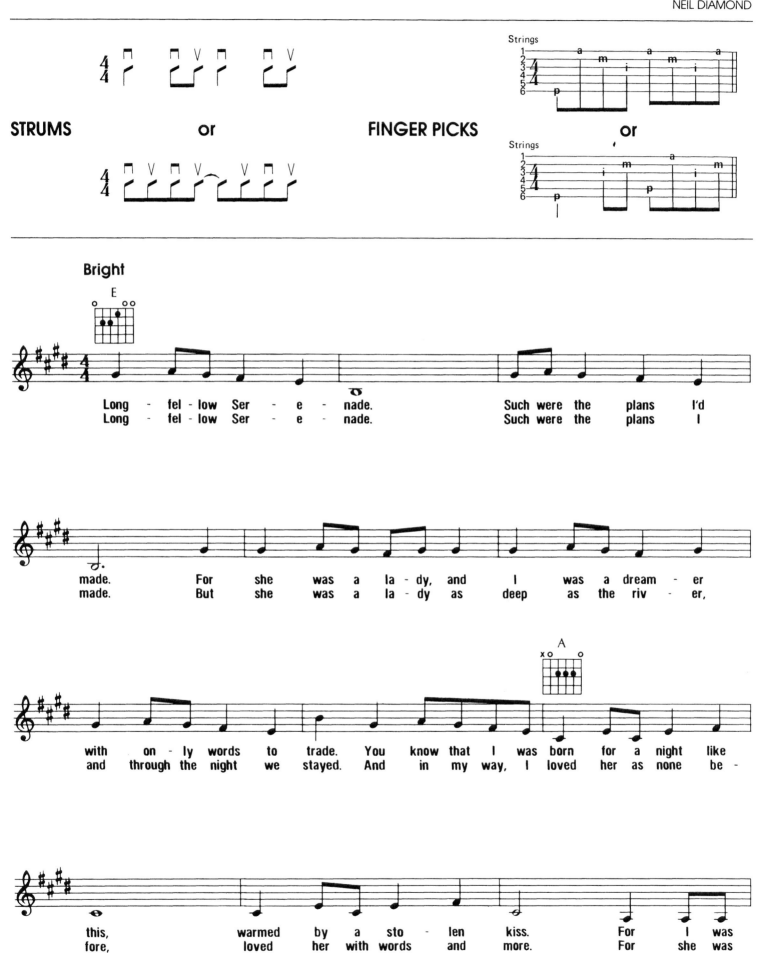

lone - ly,   and she was lone - ly.⎰
lone - ly,   and I   was lone - ly.⎱

Ride,   come on ba - by,

ride.   Let me make your dreams

come   true.   I'll sing my song

let me sing my song.   Let me make it warm

for   you   I'll

58

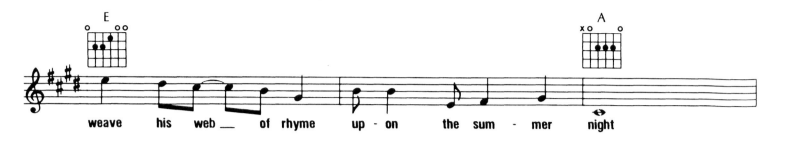

weave his web __ of rhyme up-on the sum-mer night

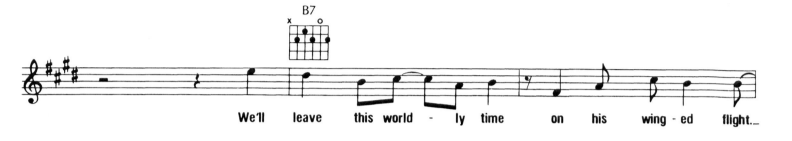

We'll leave this world - ly time on his wing-ed flight. __

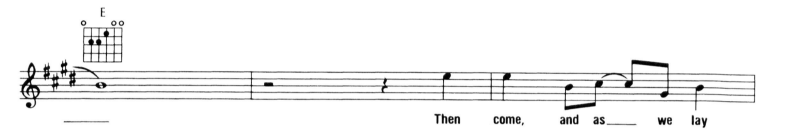

__ Then come, and as __ we lay

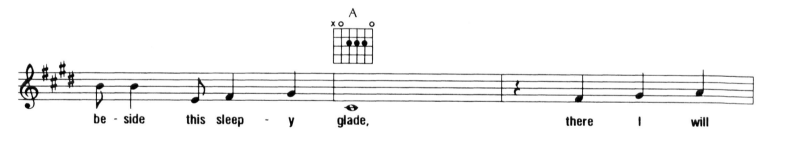

be - side this sleep - y glade, there I will

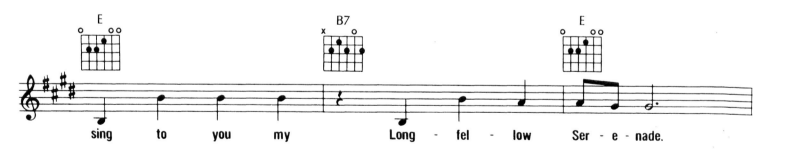

sing to you my Long - fel - low Ser - e - nade.

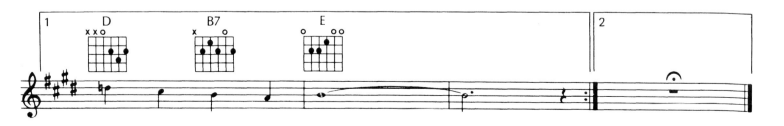

AND THE GRASS WON'T PAY NO MIND

Words and Music by
NEIL DIAMOND

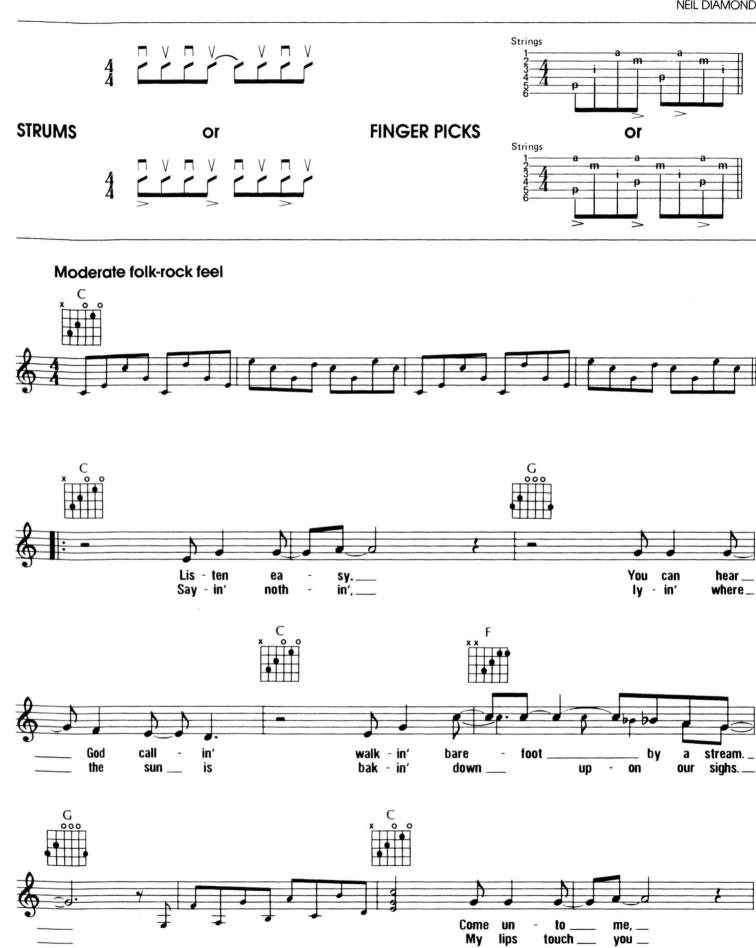

STRUMS   or   FINGER PICKS   or

Moderate folk-rock feel

Lis - ten   ea - sy. ___   You   can   hear ___
Say - in'   noth - in', ___   ly - in'   where ___

___ God   call - in'   walk - in'   bare - foot ___   by   a   stream. ___
___ the   sun ___   is   bak - in'   down ___   up - on   our   sighs.

___   Come   un - to ___   me, ___
___   My   lips   touch ___   you ___

your hair soft - ly fall - in' on my face __
with their soft __ wet kiss - es; your hands gen -

___ as in a dream. __
tle in re - ply. __ And the

time will be our time. And the

grass won't pay no mind.

mind. Child, touch my soul __

___ with your cries, __ and the mu - sic will know __ what we've found. __

61

as you lay ___ sleep-in' in my heart.___

And the time will be our

time. And the grass won't pay no

mind. No, the grass won't pay no

mind.

STARGAZER

Words and Music by
NEIL DIAMOND

STRUMS   or   FINGER PICKS   or

Moderately, with a lilt

Star - gaz - er, _____ you with your head in the heav -

- ens, you'll nev - er get by _____ walk - in' that high _____ off the

ground.

Moon - dream - er, _____
Star - gaz - er, _____

SOLITARY MAN

Words and Music by
NEIL DIAMOND

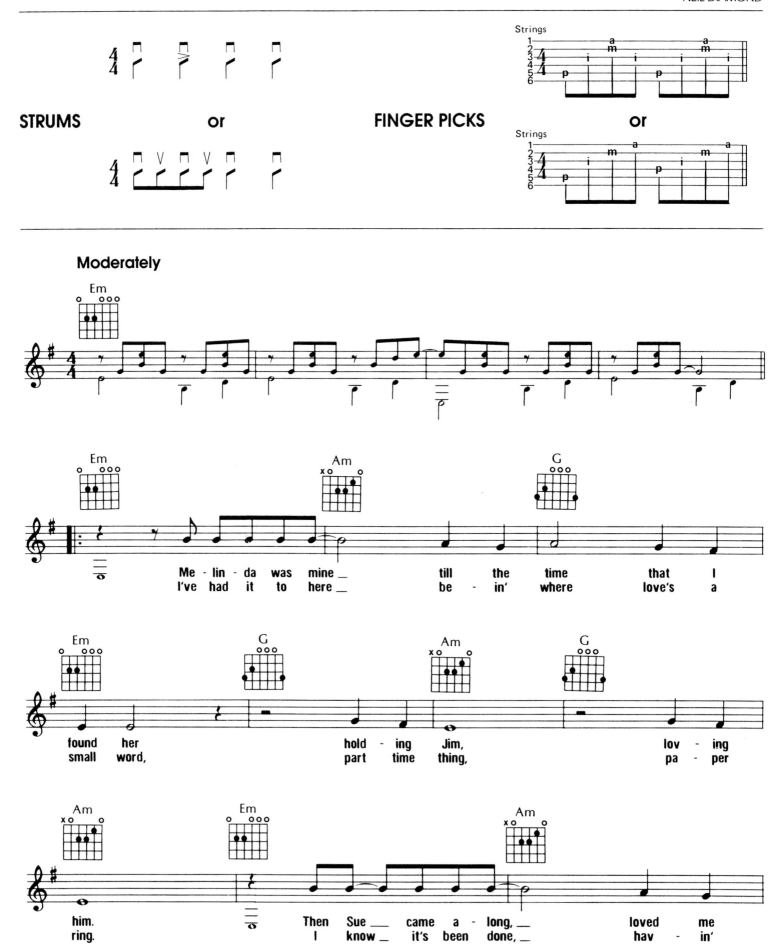

strong ___ that's what I thought.   Me and Sue,
one ___ girl who'll love me,   right or wrong,

but that died too. _____
weak or strong. _____

Don't know that I will, ___ but un - til I can

find me   the girl___ who'll stay___ and won't

play games be - hind me,   I'll be what I

am: a sol - i - tar - y man,

LADY-OH
(Baby-Oh)

Words and Music by
NEIL DIAMOND

SKYBIRD

(From JONATHAN LIVINGSTON SEAGULL, the film by Hall Bartlett)

Words and Music by
NEIL DIAMOND

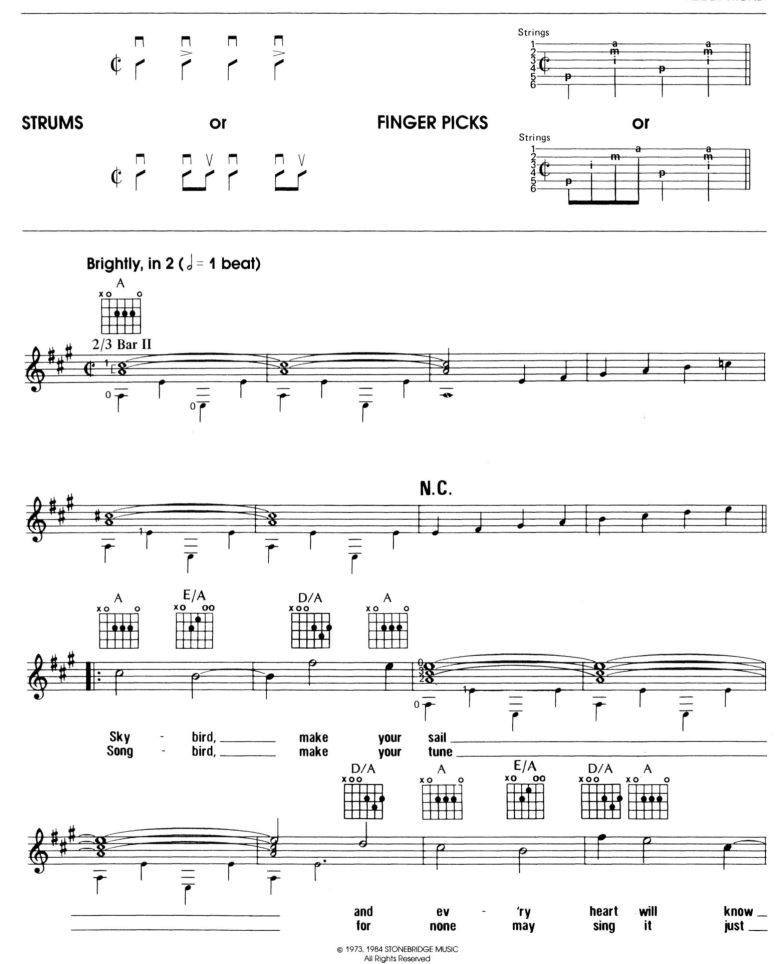

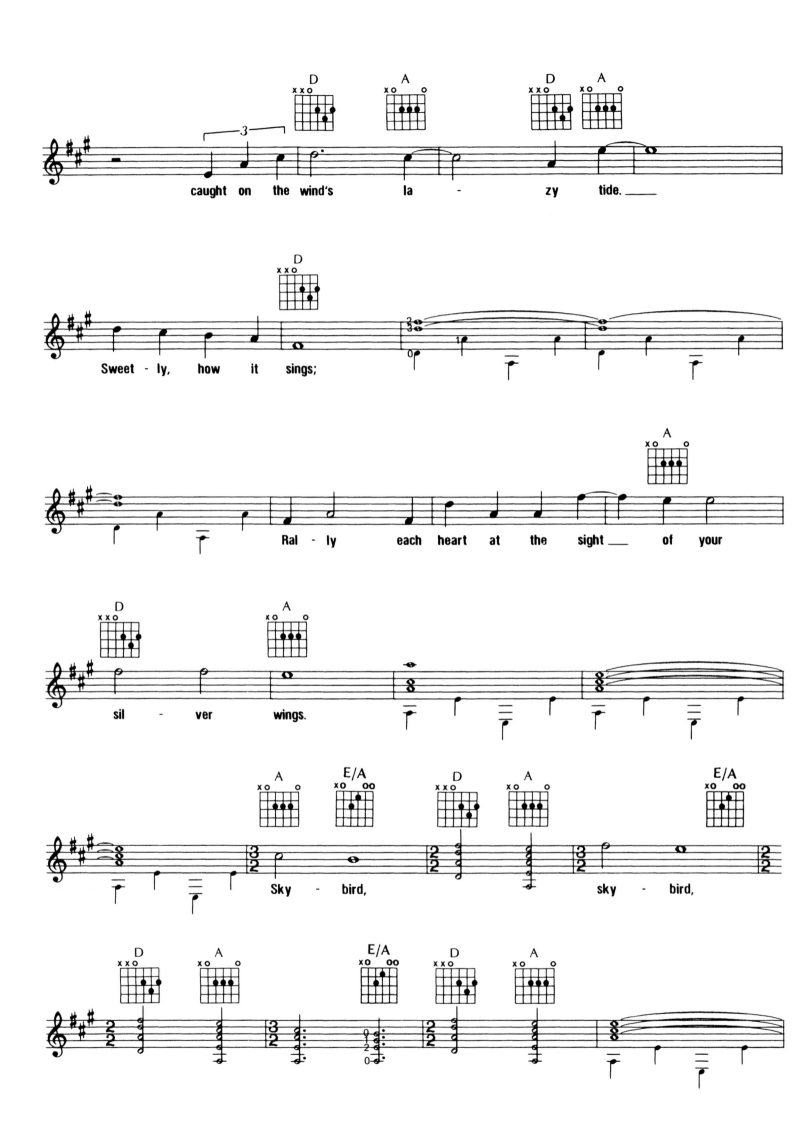

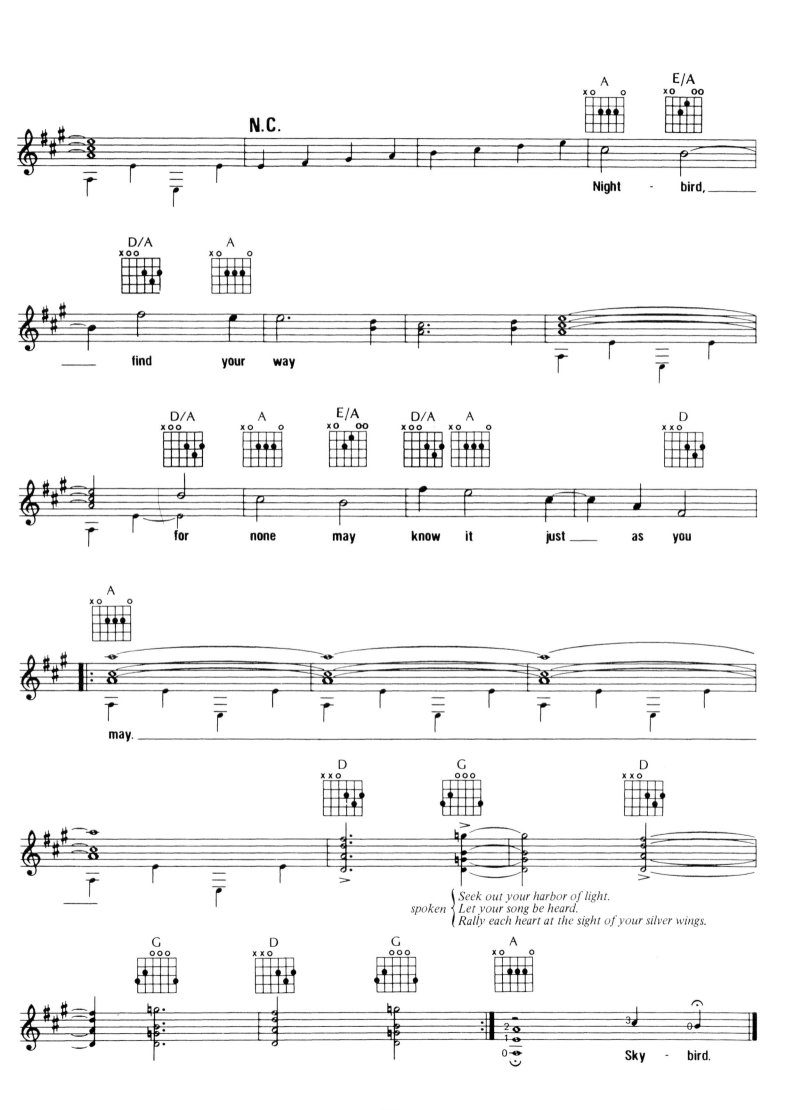

SAY MAYBE

Words and Music by
NEIL DIAMOND

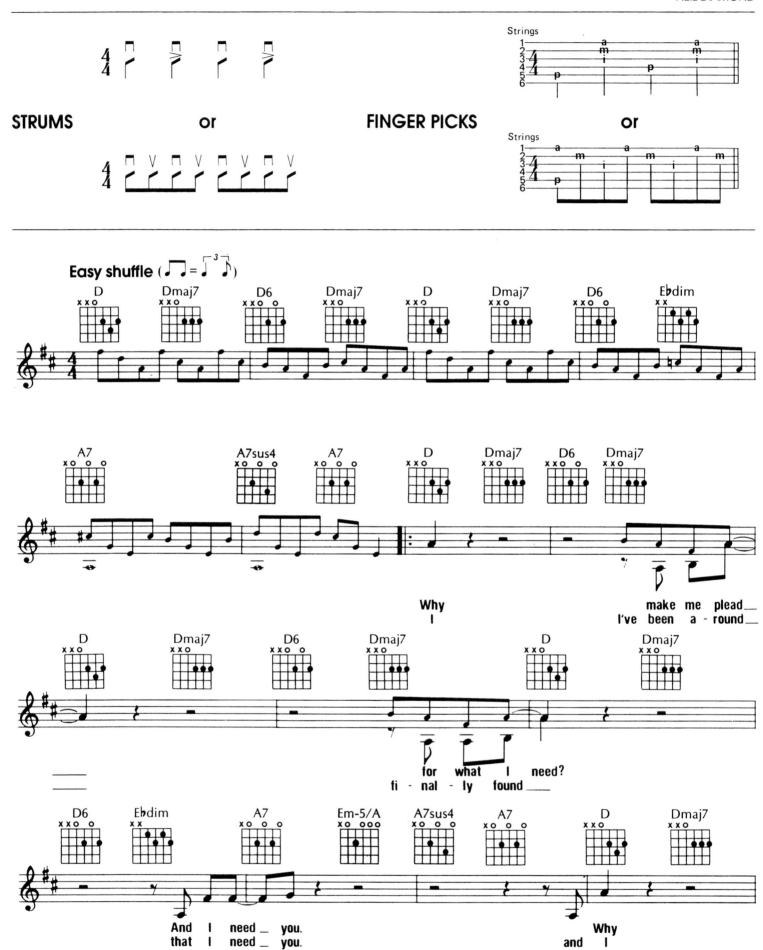

79

AND THE SINGER SINGS HIS SONG

Words and Music by
NEIL DIAMOND

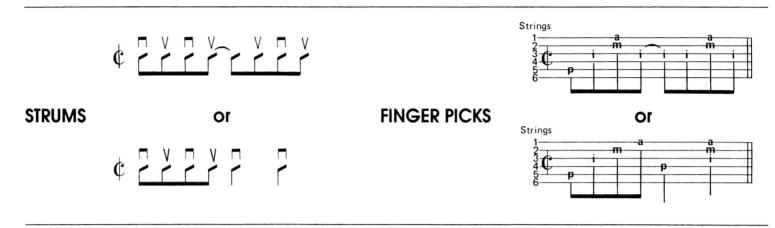

STRUMS　　　　or　　　　　**FINGER PICKS**　　　　or

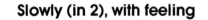

Slowly (in 2), with feeling

H.O.

Young　　　it　　was,　　　　　　　　　　true　　　it

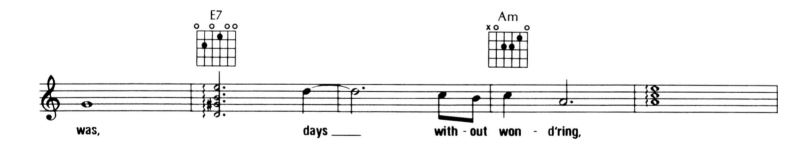

was,　　　　　　　days ____　　with - out won - d'ring,

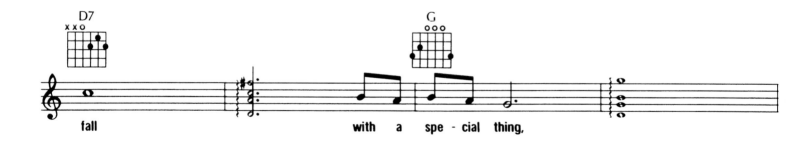

fall　　　　　　　　with　a　spe - cial thing,

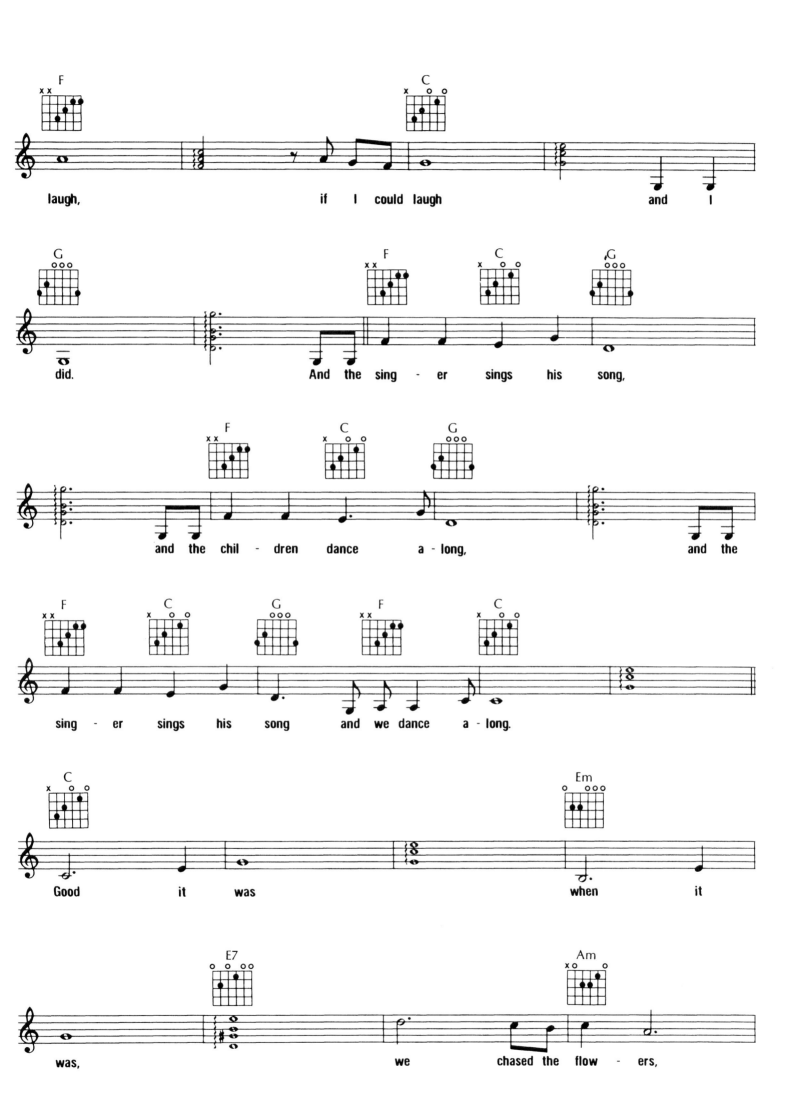

laugh,   if I could laugh   and I

did.   And the sing - er sings his song,

and the chil - dren dance a - long,   and the

sing - er sings his song   and we dance a - long.

Good   it was   when   it

was,   we   chased the flow - ers,

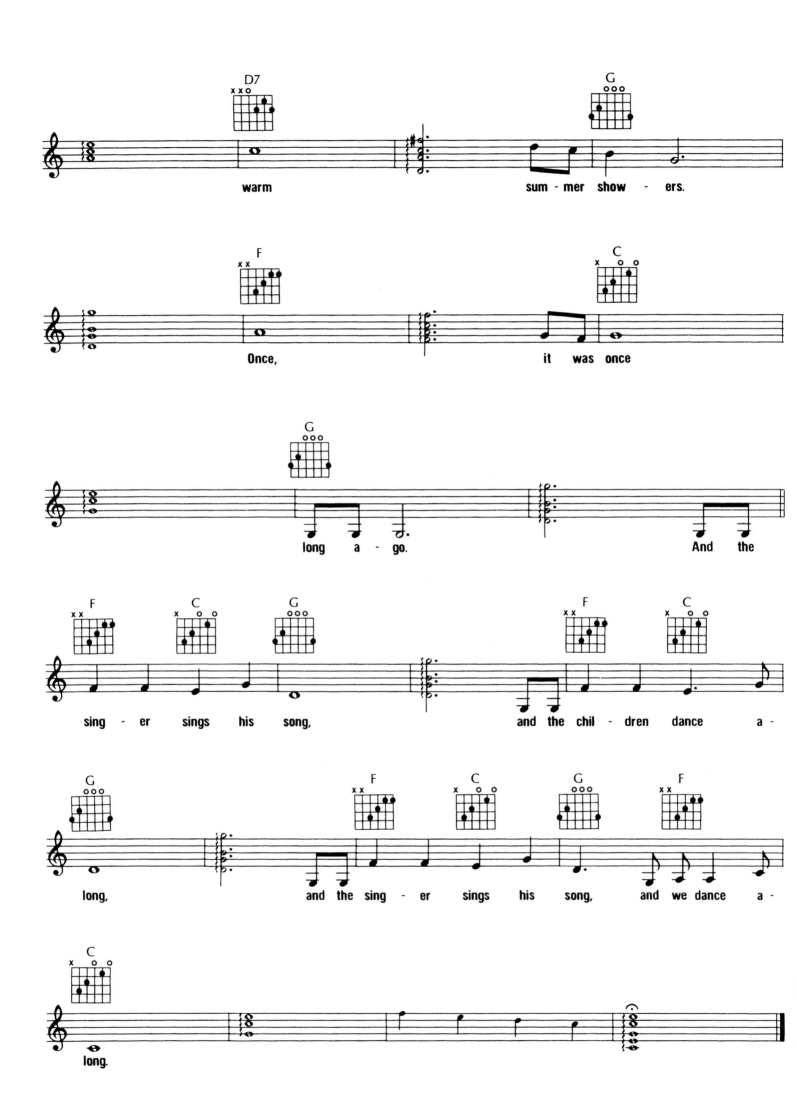

STONES

Words and Music by
NEIL DIAMOND

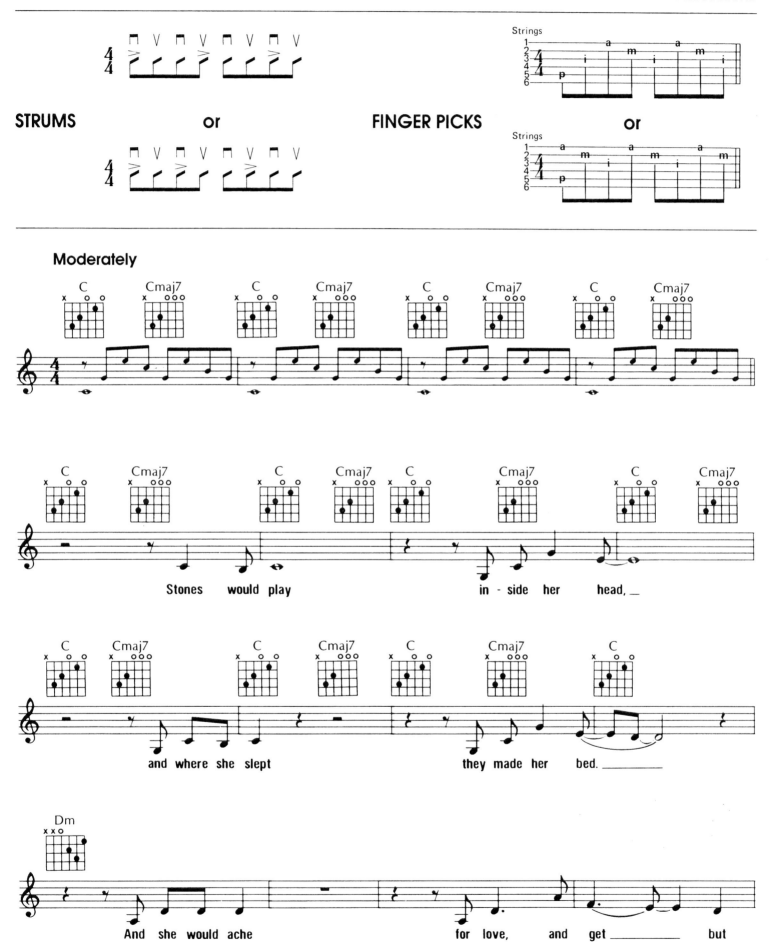

STRUMS   or   FINGER PICKS   or

ON THE WAY TO THE SKY

Words and Music by
NEIL DIAMOND & CAROLE BAYER SAGER

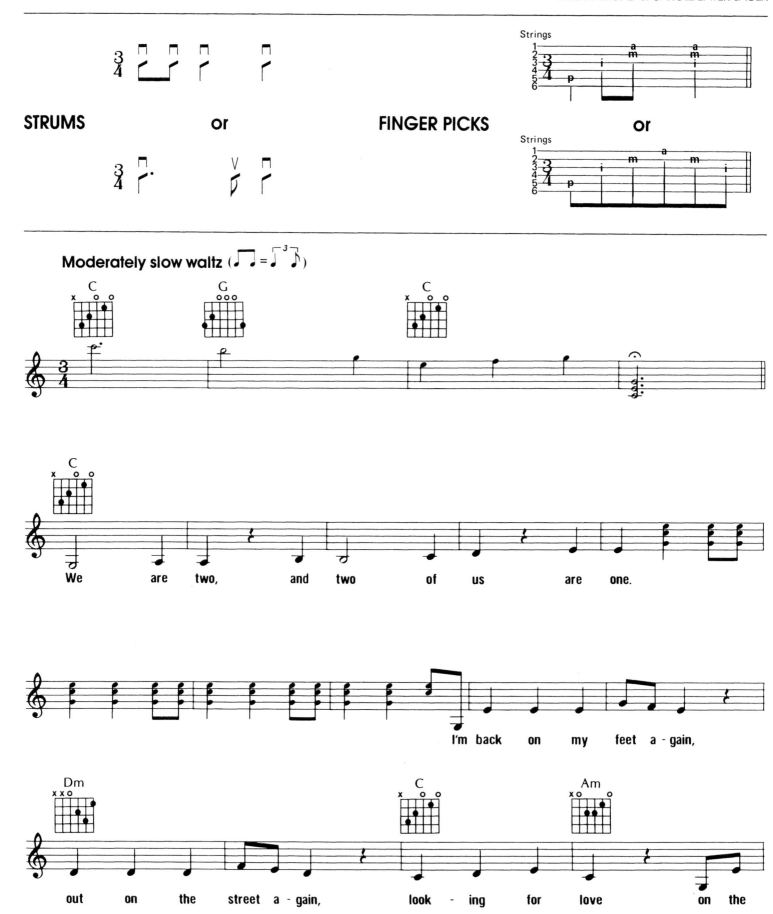

We are two, and two of us are one.

I'm back on my feet a-gain,

out on the street a-gain, look-ing for love on the

long. There's no way — to count or to meas-ure — the cost of the

in - no - cence lost on the way to the sky, to the sky.

We are two and two of us are

one. But may - be two of

us can be e - nough _____ to get it done.

song, we pit - y ____ the poor one, the shy, the un - sure one who

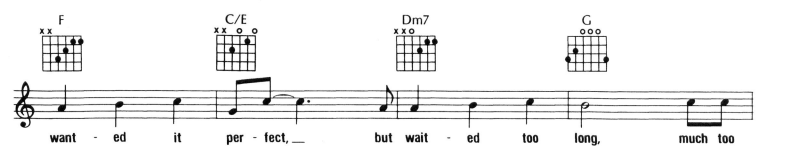

want - ed it per - fect, __ but wait - ed too long, much too

long. I'm

back on my feet a - gain, I'm

out on the street a - gain,

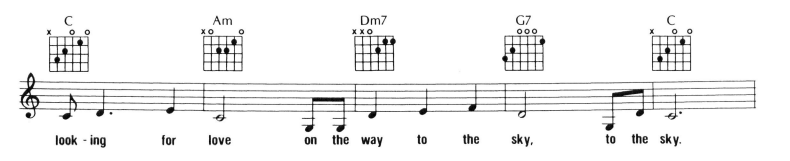

look - ing for love on the way to the sky, to the sky.

MORNINGSIDE
(For My Children)

Words and Music by
NEIL DIAMOND

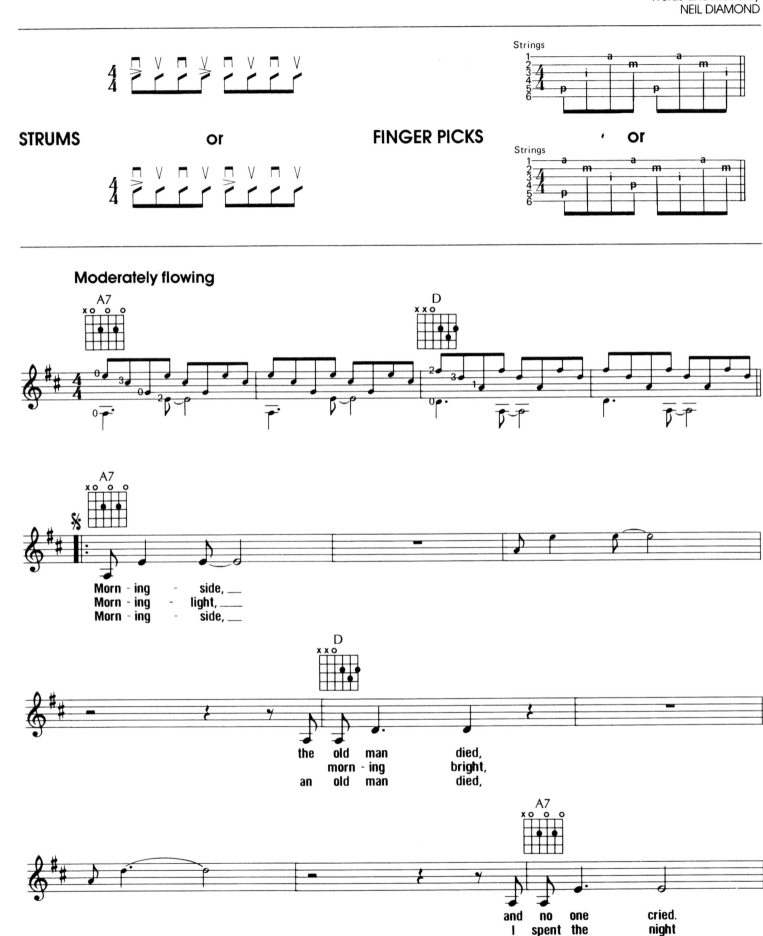

They
with
He

D   G

sim - ply turned ___ a - way. _____ And when he died ___
dreams that make __ you weep. _____ Morn - ing time, __
sure - ly died ___ a - lone. _____ And truth is sad ___

he left a ta - ble made of
wash a - way the sad - ness from of these
for not a child ___ would claim the

D

nails and pride, _____ and ___ with his hands__
eyes of mine, _____ for I re - call ___
gift he had. _____ The words __ he carved __

A7

_____ he carved ___ these words in - side:
_____ the words _ an old man signed:
_____ be - came __ his ep - i - taph:

D

"For my chil - dren."

Lyrics: (Spoken) And the

legs were shaped with his hands

and the top made of oaken wood,

and the children that sat around this great table touched it

with their laughter.   Ah, and that was good.

92

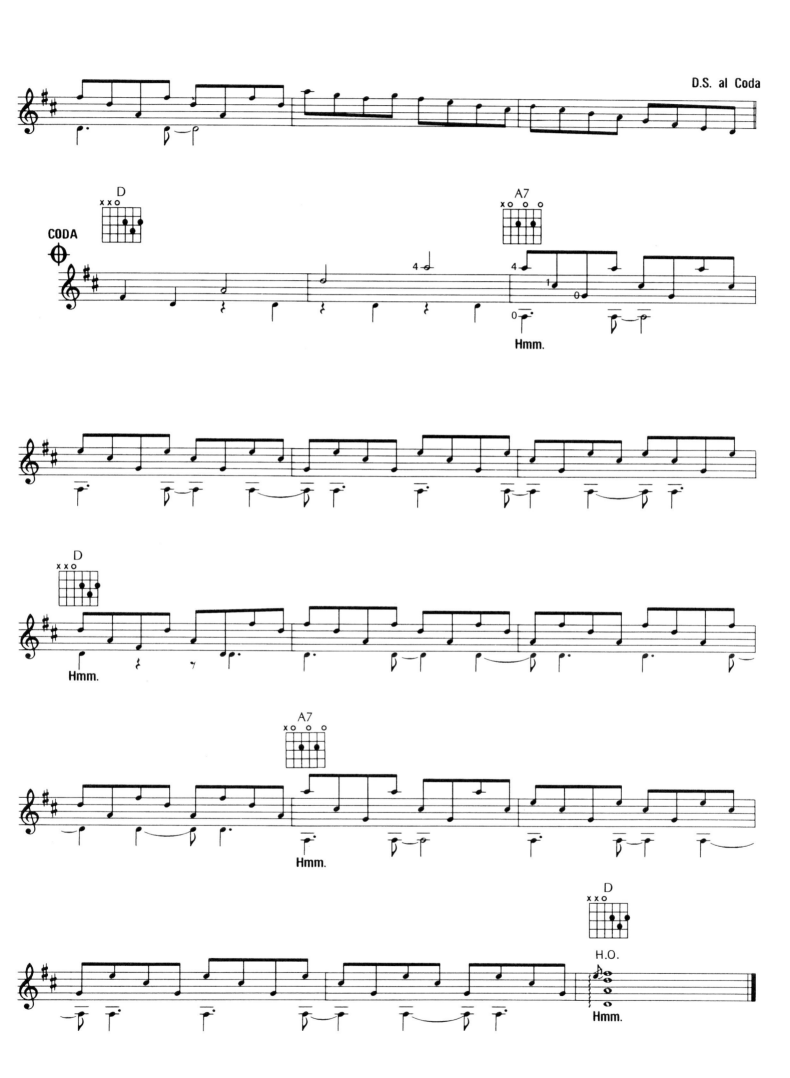

93

IF I NEVER KNEW YOUR NAME

Words and Music by
NEIL DIAMOND

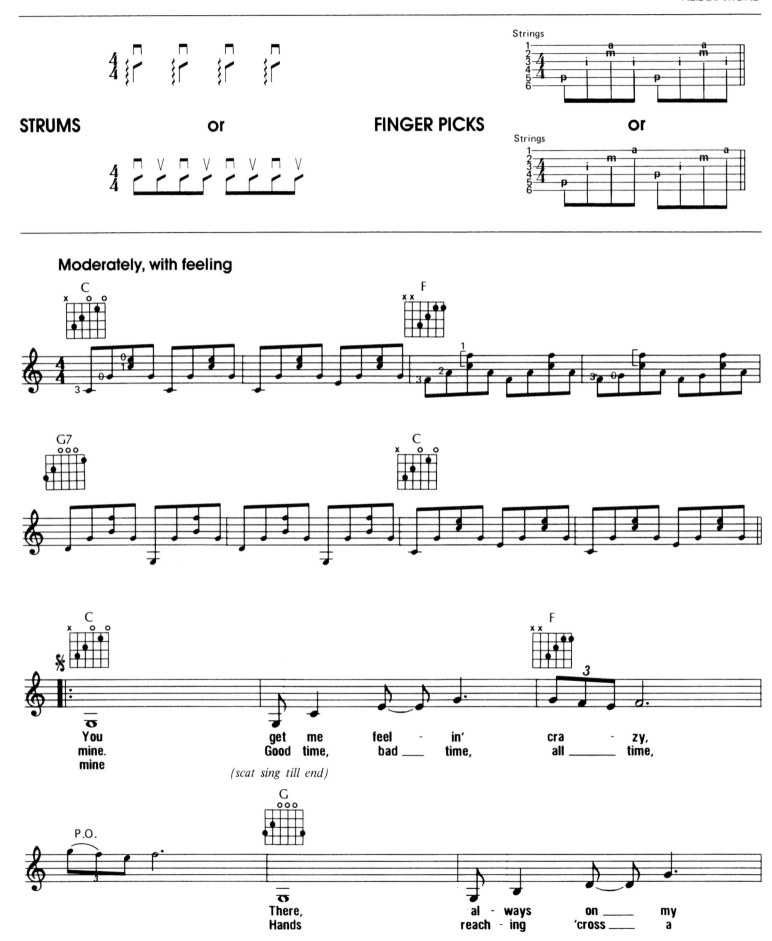

I GOT THE FEELIN'
(Oh No, No)

Words and Music by
NEIL DIAMOND

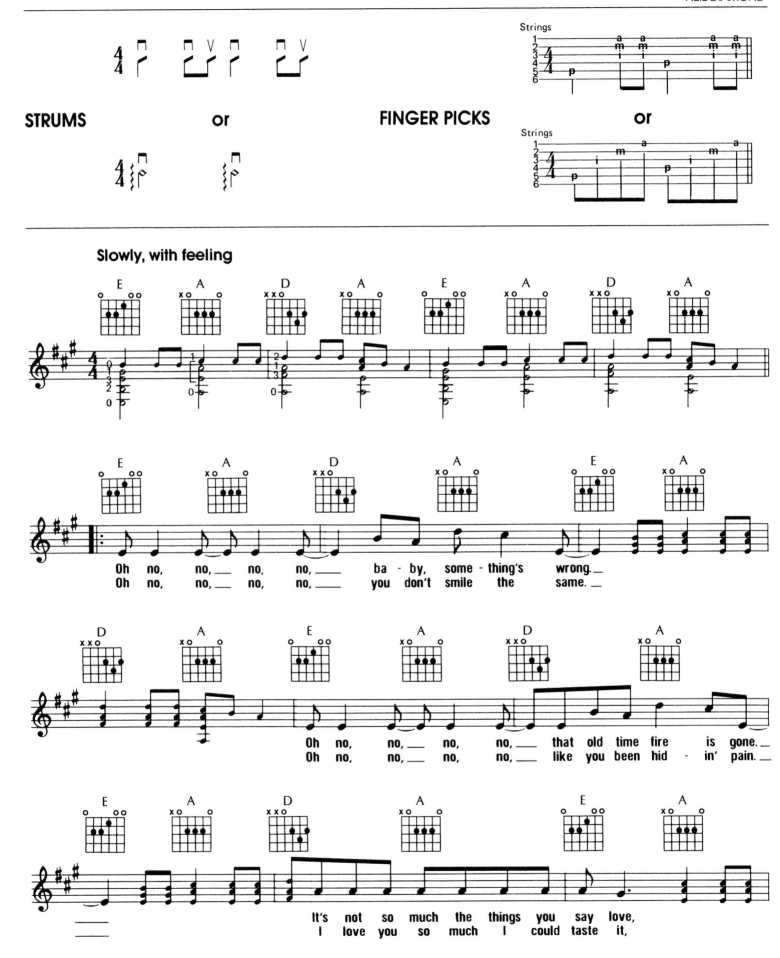

STRUMS   or   FINGER PICKS   or

Slowly, with feeling

Oh no, no,___ no, no,___ ba - by, some - thing's wrong.___
Oh no, no,___ no, no,___ you don't smile the same. __

Oh no, no,___ no, no,___ that old time fire is gone.
Oh no, no,___ no, no,___ like you been hid - in' pain.

It's not so much the things you say love,
I love you so much I could taste it,

CHERRY, CHERRY

Words and Music by
NEIL DIAMOND

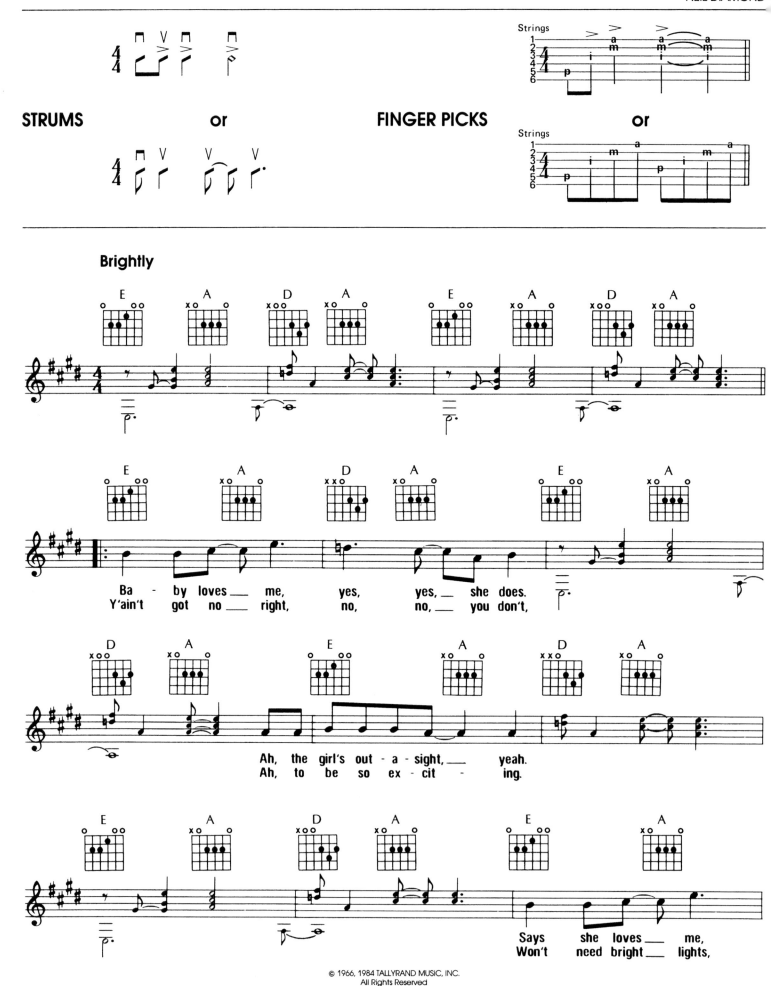

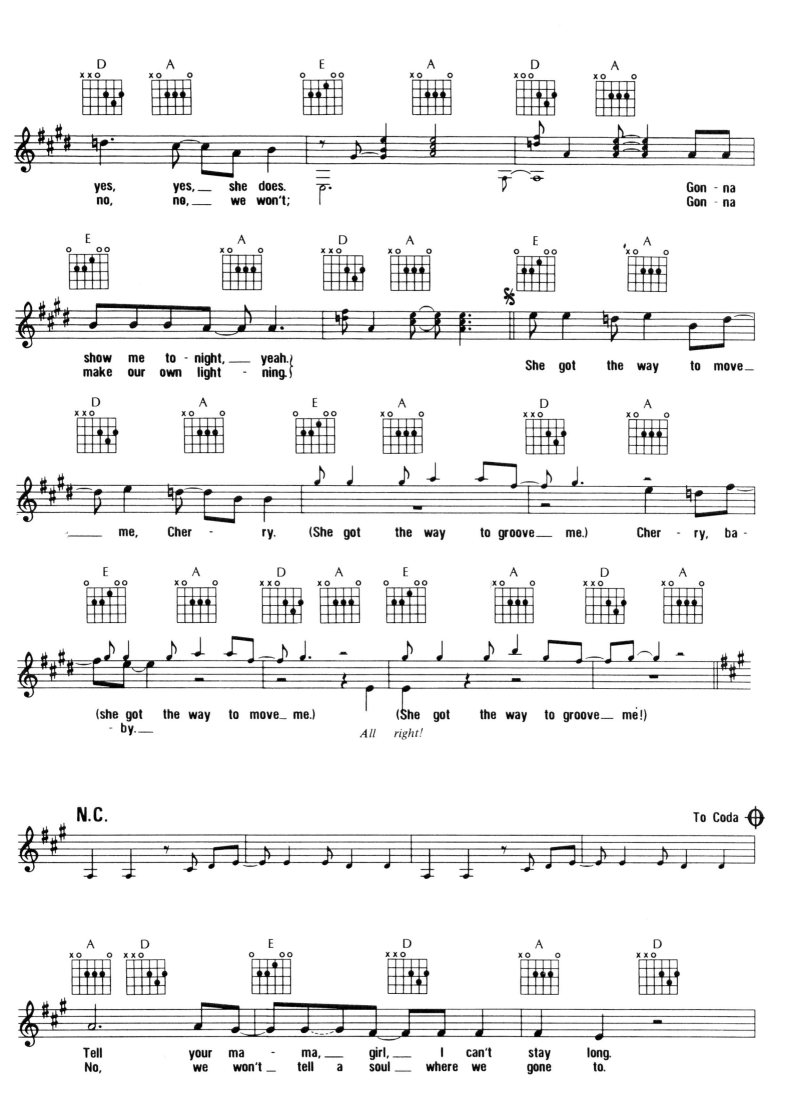

BE
(From JONATHAN LIVINGSTON SEAGULL, the film by Hall Bartlett)

Words and Music by
NEIL DIAMOND

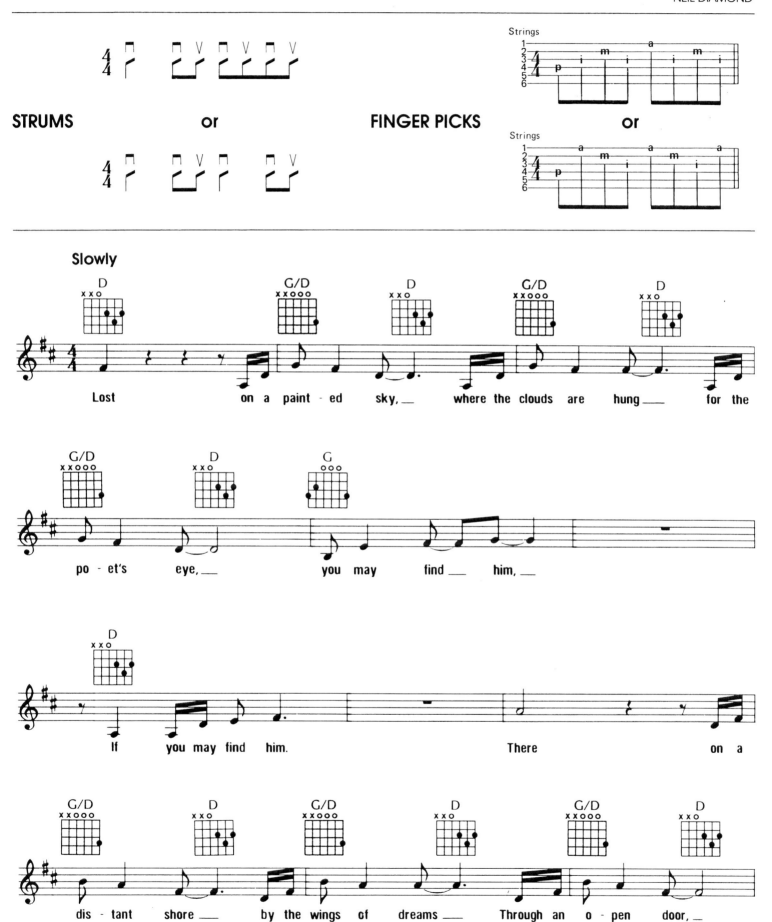

G A
you may know him, if you may.
A7 D G/D D
Be as a page that aches for a word which speaks on a theme that is time-less while the
G D
sun god will make for your day. Sing
G/D D
as a song in search of a voice that is si-lent, and the
G D
one God will make for your way.
Fine

And we dance _ to a whis-pered voice, ___ o-ver-heard by the soul, un-der-took by the heart, and you may know _ it, ___ if you may know it.

While the sand would be-come the stone, ___ which be-gat the spark, ___ turned to liv-ing bone. _ Ho-ly, Ho-ly, ___ Sanc-tus, ___ Sanc-tus. ___

D.S. al Fine

HOLLY HOLY

Words and Music by
NEIL DIAMOND

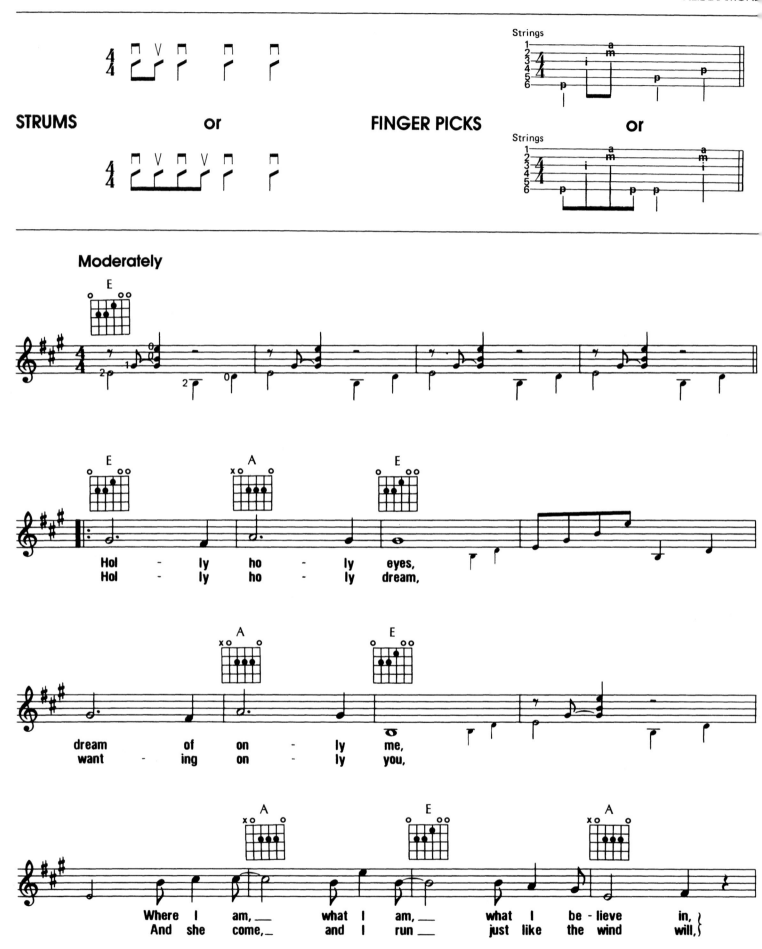

Hol - ly ho - ly.

(Sing) Sing _ a song. _ (Sing) Sing _ a song of

songs. (Sing) Sing _ it out, _ sing it strong, _

Sing it! Sing it! Sing it! Yeah!

Yeah!

Call the sun in the dead _ of the night _ and the sun's _ gon-na rise _ in the sky. _

filled with to - mor - row,   Hol - ly ho -

D.S. al Coda

CODA

- ly.   Hol - ly   Ho - ly

dream,   dream   of   on - ly

you.   Hol — hol - ly ho -   ho - ly sun,—
Hol — hol - ly ho -   ly rain,—

Hol - ly

ho - ly love.

GITCHY GOOMY

Words and Music by
NEIL DIAMOND

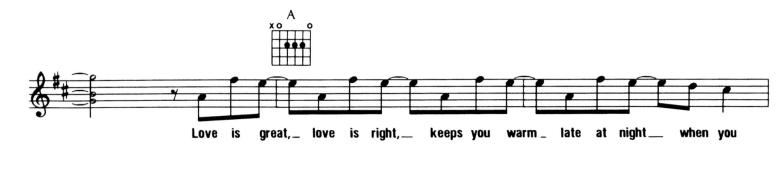

Love is great,__ love is right,__ keeps you warm__ late at night__ when you

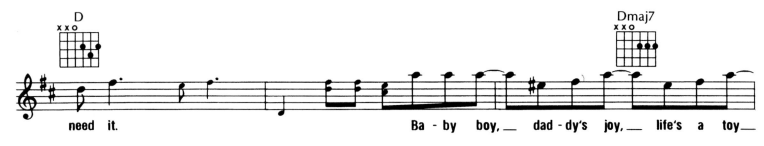

need it. Ba - by boy,__ dad - dy's joy,__ life's a toy__

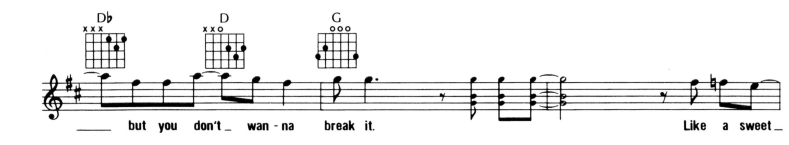

____ but you don't __ wan - na break it. Like a sweet__

____ sym - pho - ny,__ all you need __ is the key, __ you can play it.

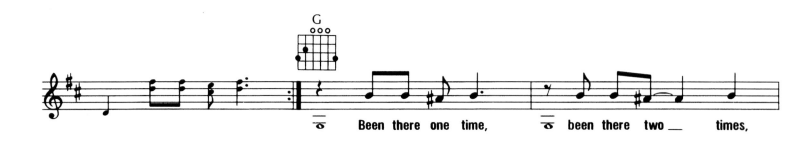

Been there one time, been there two __ times,

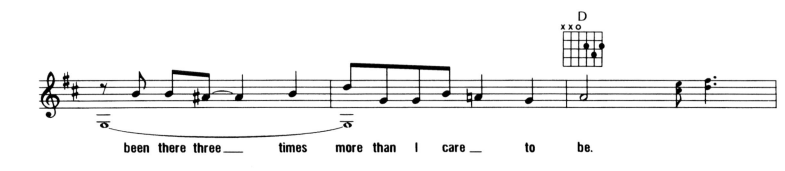

been there three__ times more than I care __ to be.

111

CANTA LIBRE

Words and Music by
NEIL DIAMOND

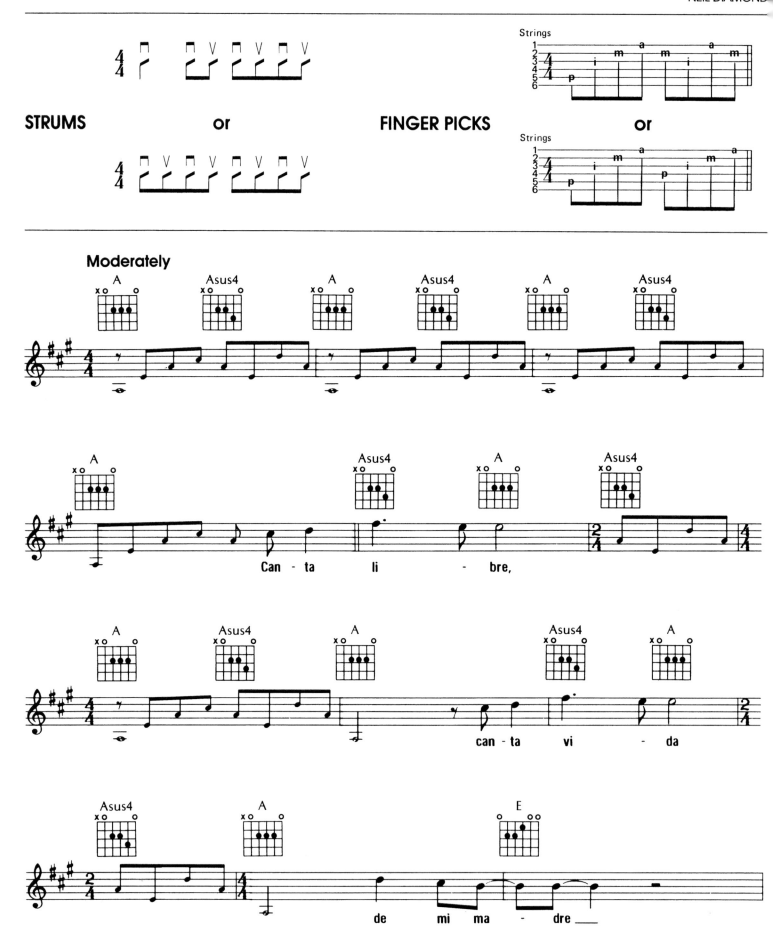

STRUMS   or   FINGER PICKS   or

Moderately

Can - ta   li   -   bre,

can - ta   vi   -   da

de   mi   ma - dre ___

makes me feel ___ like a young ___ bird
ev - 'ry song ___ with its own ___ kind of

fly - ing.
mean - ing.

'Cross my mind ___
Cleanse the soul ___

___ and lay - in' in my bed, ___
___ and wash a - way the pain, ___

keeps me a - way ___ from the thought ___ of dy - ing.
bap - tized ___ by ___ the song ___ that you're sing - ing.

Can - ta li - bre;
Can - ta li - bre;

can - ta vi - da
can - ta la vi - da

de mi
siempre con -

madre
y mi pa - dre.

mi - go.
Can - ta

li - bre. ___

(Spoken) Can - ta libre.

Can - ta vi - da

de mi madre y mi padre. Can - ta mi corazon, para los niños, y sus niños.

Can - ta libre.

DONE TOO SOON

Words and Music by
NEIL DIAMOND

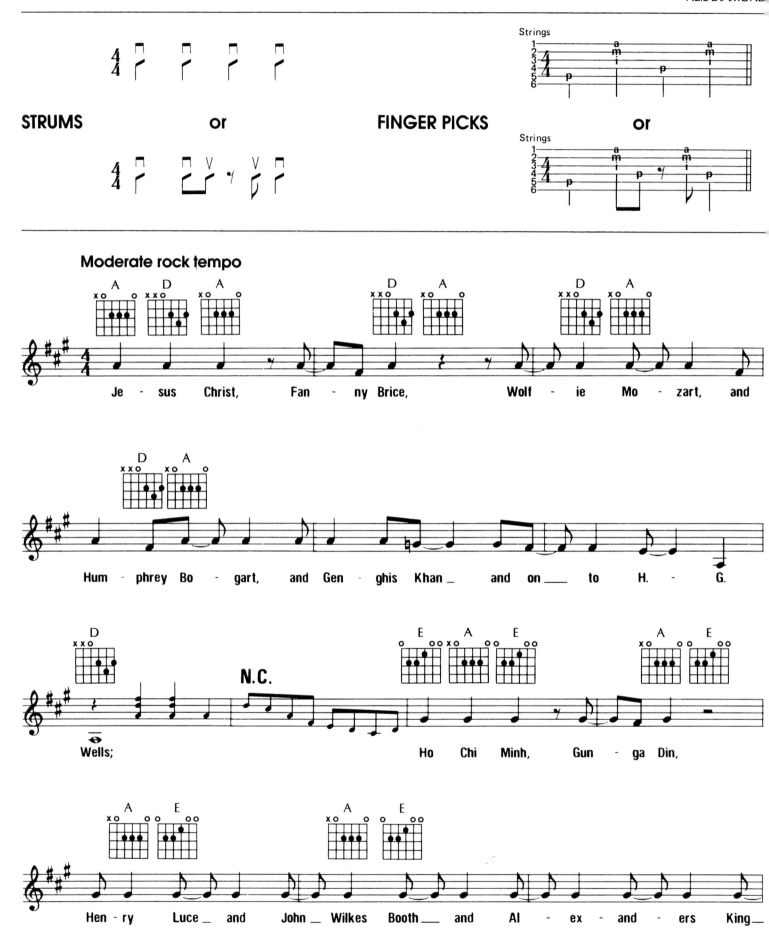

Rous - seau, Sho - lom A - leich - em, and Car - yl Chess - man, Al-

- an Freed __ and Bus - ter Kea - ton, too. __

(Harmonic)
② 12 fr.
And

Rubato   A tempo

each one there has one thing shared: They have sweat - ed be - neath the same __

118

CRUNCHY GRANOLA SUITE

Words and Music by
NEIL DIAMOND

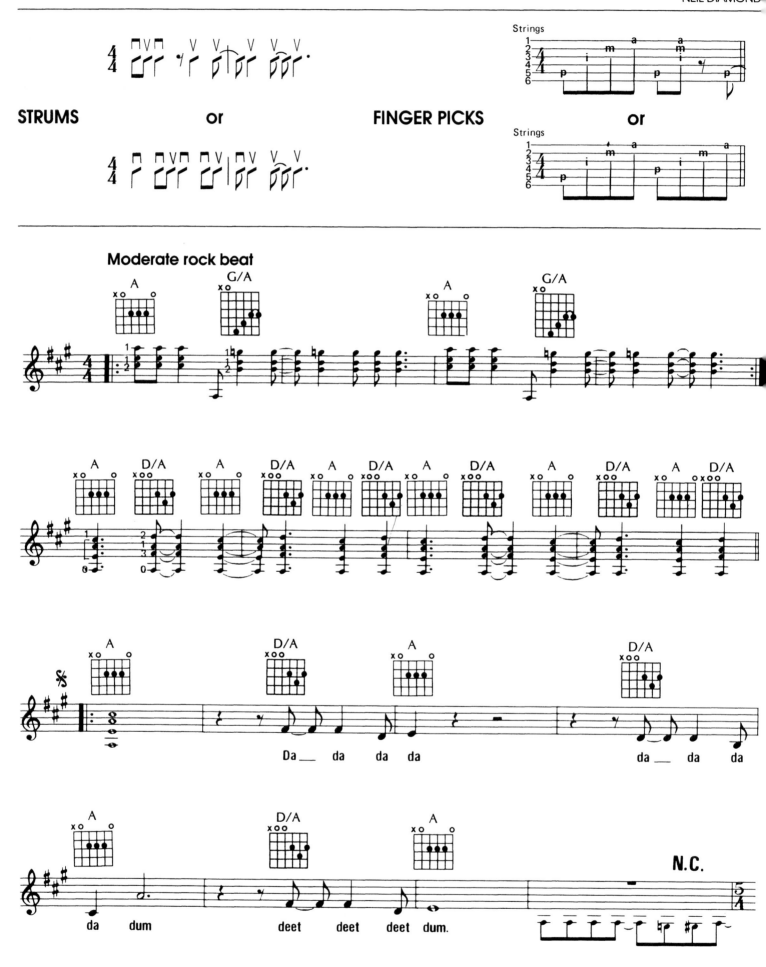

STRUMS   or   FINGER PICKS   or

Moderate rock beat

Da __ da da da   da __ da da

da dum   deet deet deet dum.

N.C.

Sing it out,   all

right.

Da __ da da da   da __ da da

da dum __   deet __ deet deet dum.

(Spoken) I'll have a double, please!

HOME IS A WOUNDED HEART

Words and Music by
NEIL DIAMOND

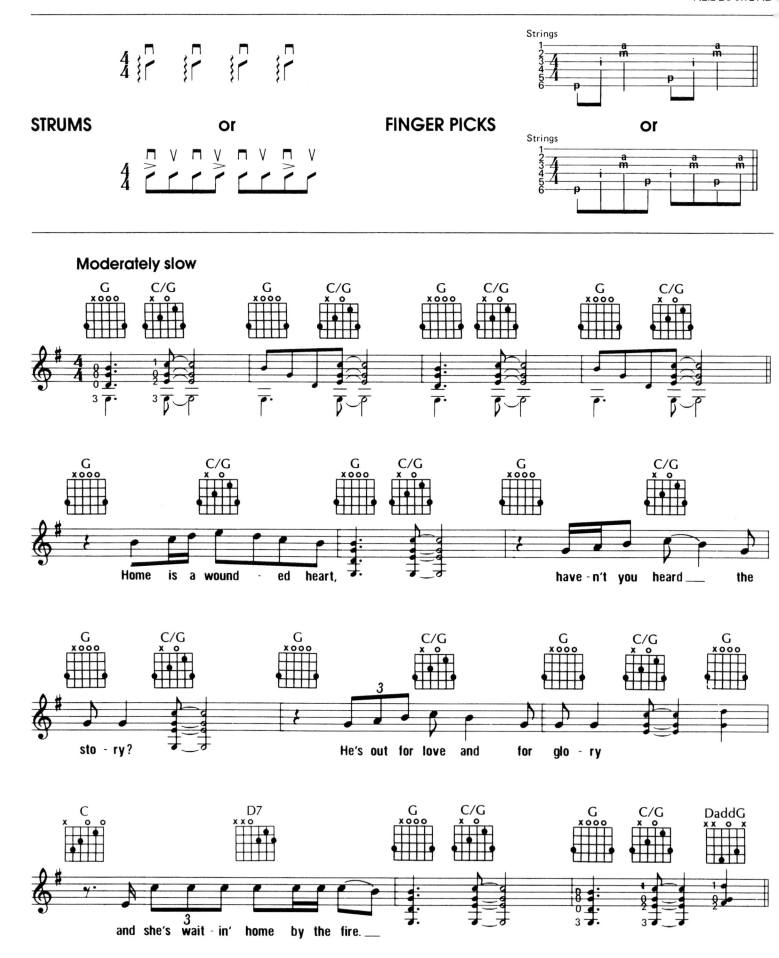

STRUMS   or   **FINGER PICKS**   or

Moderately slow

Home is a wound - ed heart,   have - n't you heard ___ the

sto - ry?   He's out for love and for glo - ry

and she's wait - in' home by the fire. ___

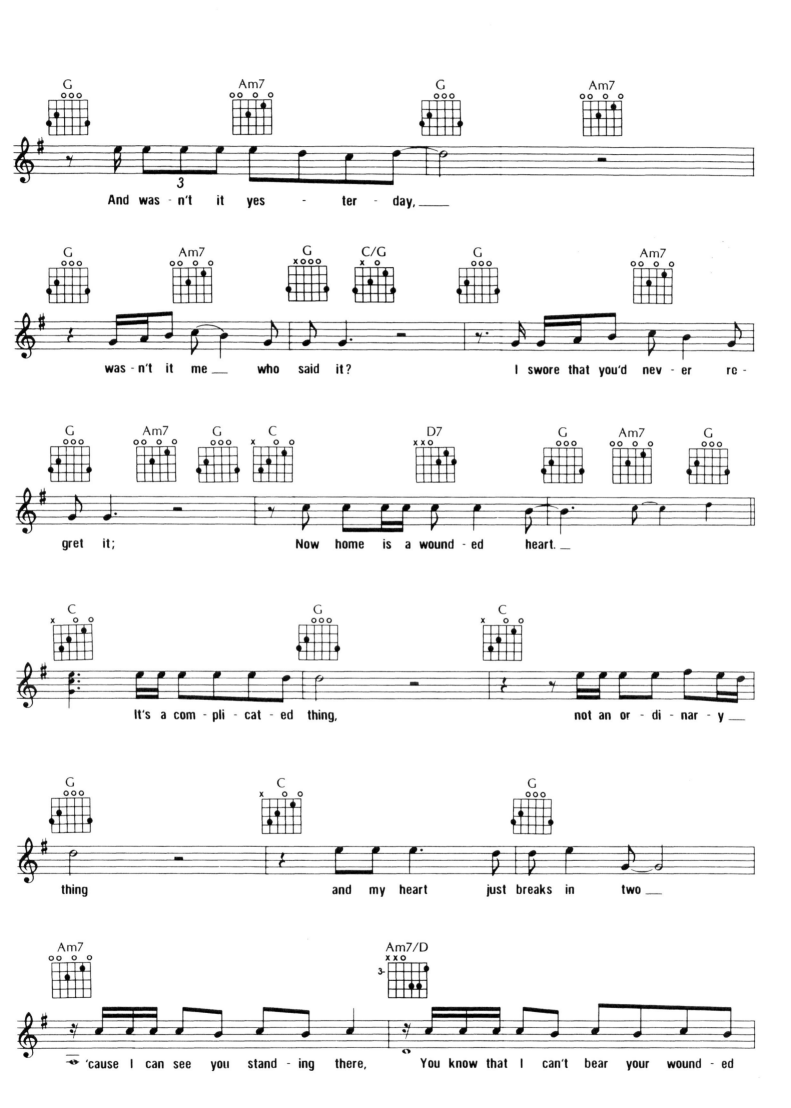

WALK ON WATER

Words and Music by
NEIL DIAMOND

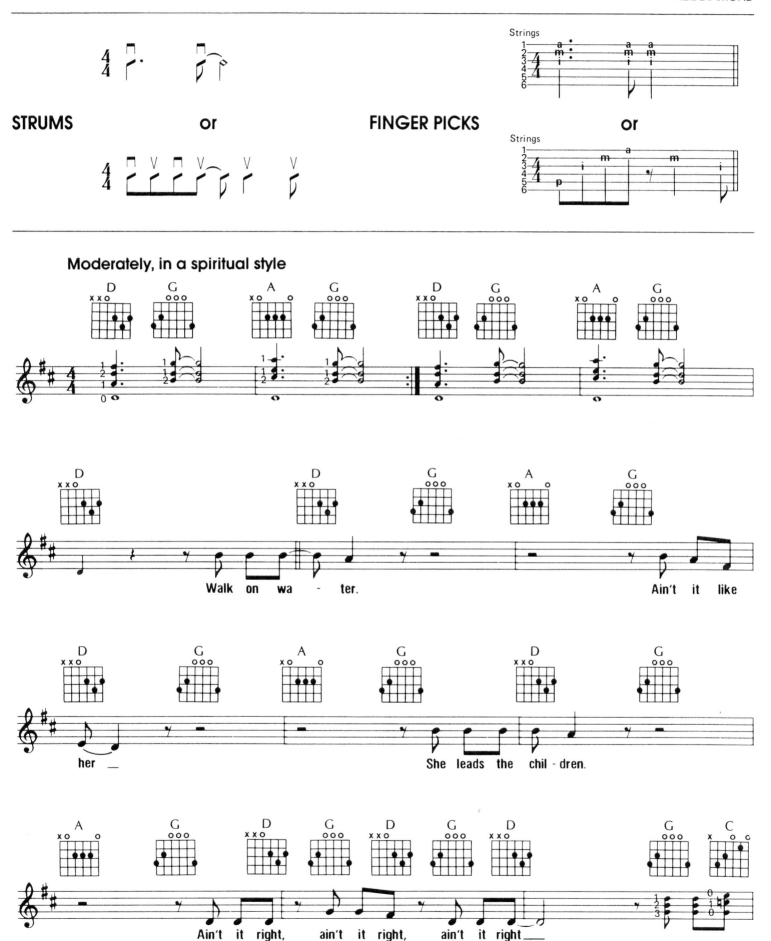

Walk on wa - ter. Ain't it like her ___ She leads the chil - dren. Ain't it right, ain't it right, ain't it right ___

Faster with a gospel feel

KENTUCKY WOMAN

Words and Music by
NEIL DIAMOND

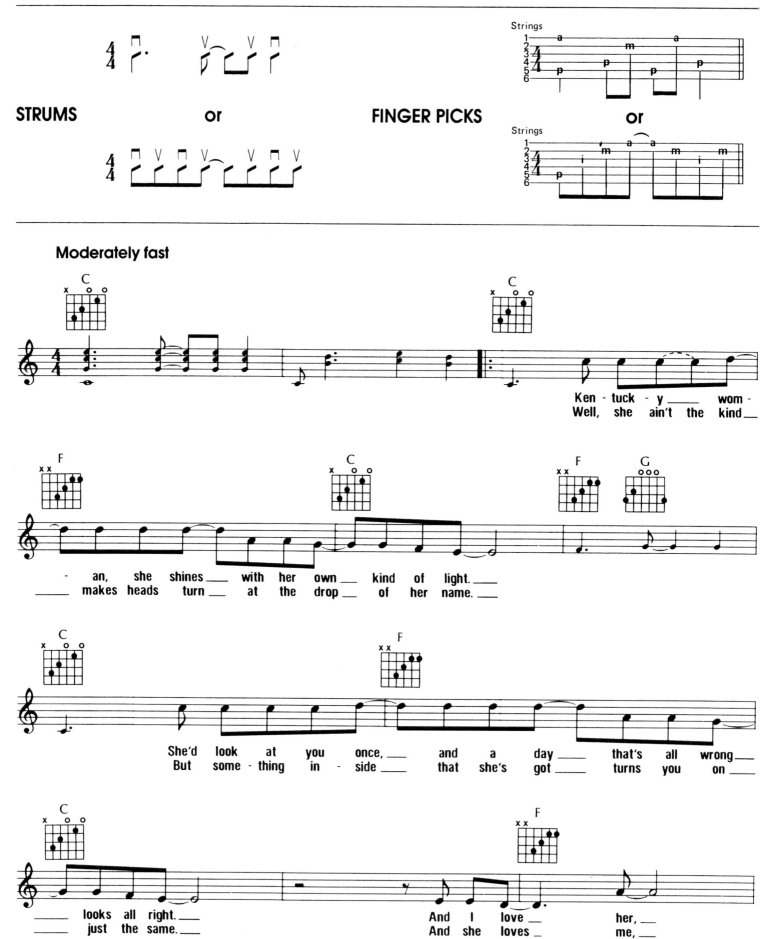

God ___ knows, I love her. ___
God ___ knows, she loves me. ___

Ken - tuck - y wom -

- an,

if she get to know you, ___

she goin' to own you,

Ken - tuck - y wom -

- an. ___

I don't want much, ___

the good Lord's earth ___

___ be - neath my feet. ___ A gen - tle touch _

131

from that one girl __ and life __ is   sweet and   good. __

Ain't no   doubt __   I'm talk - in' a - bout __   Ken - tuck - y   wom -

- an.   If she get to know you, ___   she goin' to

own you.   Ken - tuck - y wom - an. ___

Ken - tuck - y wom - an, ___   Ken - tuck - y wom -

- an, ___   Ken - tuck - y wom - an.

I'M A BELIEVER

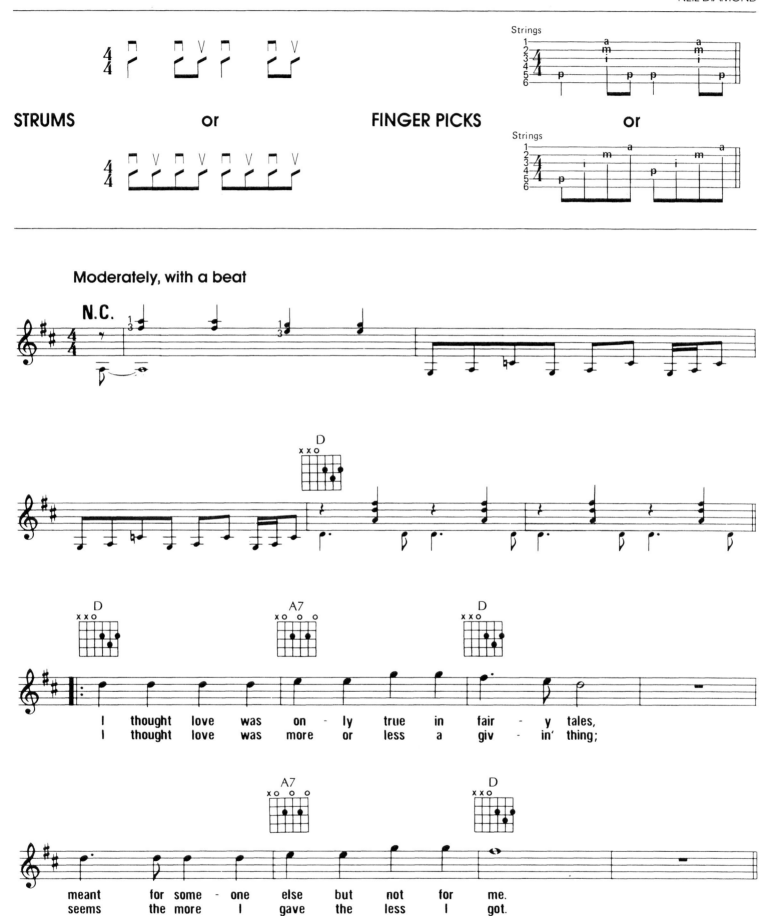

Words and Music by
NEIL DIAMOND

STRUMS   or   FINGER PICKS   or

Moderately, with a beat

I thought love was on-ly true in fair-y tales,
I thought love was more or less a giv-in' thing;

meant for some-one else but not for me.
seems the more I gave the less I got.